Mother to Mother

Kathy McCue

FNP, IBCLC

Mother to Mother: What New Mothers Want You to
Know About Birth and Breastfeeding

Kathleen F. McCue, RN, MS, FNP-BC, IBCLC

© Copyright 2012

Cover design by Erin McCue

Hale Publishing, L.P.

1712 N. Forest St.

Amarillo, TX 79106-7017

806-376-9900

800-378-1317

www.iBreastfeeding.com

Library of Congress Control Number: 2011945935

ISBN-13: 978-0-9847746-1-6

Printing and Binding: Malloy, Inc.

Dedicated to mothers everywhere who work hard to get through each day, and then get up the next day and do it all over again.

Acknowledgements

I want to express my heartfelt gratitude and respect to the thousands of mothers who have shaped my work and helped me learn what's important to teach other moms. These women, along with my own children, Adam and Erin, have given true purpose to my life's journey.

Deepest thanks to the mothers who took time out of their busy days to share their wisdom. I hope that their knowledge and sisterhood will make the childbirth experience more rewarding.

I am especially grateful to Hale Publishing, especially Tom Hale and Janet Rourke, for finding substance and wisdom in my work.

Finally, I would like to thank Jennifer Richards, my publicist, for her support and guidance in helping me navigate the literary waters.

Table of Contents

Foreword

A woman's journey to motherhood begins at her birth. From that day forward she is exposed to mothering based upon the voice of her own mother and other women that act as surrogate mothers. These early experiences start to shape the "mother-to-be" in two ways – they teach her what she wants to incorporate in her own mothering and what she wants to avoid. Often times, our own mothers provide us a "default" for the mothers we become. In times of stress, we instinctively tend to say something that in retrospect sounds suspiciously familiar.

"Mother-to-Mother" provides important voices that aren't heard upon one's journey to motherhood – the chorus of peers. Amazingly, friends, relatives, and even strangers feel free to bestow advice on mothers-to-be and new moms. Sometimes, there are wise words to be heard, while other times, it's best to politely nod. Motherhood is an intensely personal journey that women often have difficulty sharing with one another, especially when things aren't looking like the perfection and bliss that is expected. The mothers in these pages are honest about the good, the bad, and the ugly. There is no one way to mother, and this is perfectly reflected. One person's choices aren't the "right" ones for everyone, so having a variety of opinions looking retrospectively at their experiences provides a spectrum of options.

Kathleen McCue weaves these voices with sensitivity and provides an important collection of experiences to help any new mom on her own journey of motherhood.

Julie Bindeman, Psy-D

Introduction

Not a day goes by that a new mom, at my pediatric office, doesn't tell me she "wishes someone would have told her _____ (you fill in the blank)" prior to becoming a new mother. As I began thinking about it, I started imagining new mothers imparting that kind of knowledge, first hand, to other mothers to prevent them from experiencing the same pitfalls and mistakes. Perhaps there is a deficit in what we, as healthcare providers, find important to teach families about to embark on parenthood. Many of us are further down the reproductive road AND things have changed. There are things I don't even know to tell moms to do because my kids were born 26 years ago!

This idea is especially hitting home because I write this book as I recuperate from a robotically assisted abdominal surgery. Clearly, I'm at the other end of the reproductive cycle, but still…. As I lay in my hospital bed, I remember thinking it would have been nice for someone to tell me that they do this surgery with me partially on my head, so I would not have been surprised when I woke up looking like I had a large pumpkin on my shoulders instead of my regular sized narrow head. I did actually hear a snippet about this from the anesthesiologist, but it was really too late—there wasn't any time to process this information. I also didn't know what having my abdomen pumped full of gas would feel like, that it would hurt all the way up to my shoulders, and that I'd feel like I was having a heart attack when I changed positions in my bed. I'm not even sure what I would have done differently, but I did feel it was my right to be prepared. Perhaps I wouldn't have privately panicked and thought a pulmonary embolism was lurking in my lungs…Sheesh! It was with that feeling and sentiment in mind that I began to write this book.

I've structured the book as a questionnaire I distributed to as many mothers as I could. I asked each mom the same questions, but the responses are all unique. I also had a couple of moms who preferred to address my readers in composition form. I took whatever was offered in the spirit of not having my readers taken by surprise when they enter the new world of babies.

The email or letter and questionnaire was as follows:

> If you're receiving this email, it's because I trust you to help me gather some great information for writing my second book.
>
> The concept of this book is that there is a deluge of information out there that new moms and dads are NOT receiving prior to giving birth and breastfeeding. Moms (and dads) seem constantly shocked at many aspects of infant care and child rearing.
>
> Here's your chance to make sure new parents are never caught like a deer in the headlights again!
>
> If you can't answer all these questions, do the best you can.
>
> Humor is always appreciated though not required or expected.
>
> Part 1
>
> 1a) What's the most important bit of advice you wish you would have known prior to giving birth?
>
> 1b) What's the most important bit of advice you wish you would have known prior to breastfeeding?
>
> 2) What one thing helps more moms succeed at breastfeeding?
>
> 3) Any other suggestions or advice you know would benefit a new mom?
>
> 4) What were your biggest hurdles or obstacles to overcome and how did you overcome them?

5) What was the most unexpected part of becoming a new mother?

6) What was the best part of becoming a mother?

7) What was the worst part of your experience?

8) What is the one mistake you can save someone from making?

9) Do you have a favorite gadget you either purchased or devised?

10) Name the three most helpful coping strategies you used after giving birth.

11) What concerns did you have prior to giving birth; what were you most afraid of? How realistic were these fears?

12) What will you do differently next time or what would you have done differently if given the chance?

Part 2

1) What did your spouse, family, and/or friends do that were extremely helpful?

2) What did your spouse, family, and/or friends do that weren't so helpful?

3) What suggestions do you have for encouraging spouse, family, and/or friends to continue doing the helpful things?

4) What suggestions do you have for discouraging spouse, family, and/or friends from doing the things that weren't so helpful?

5) Were any books, classes, internet sites, etc. helpful in preparing you for childbirth and breastfeeding?

6) Were any books, classes, internet sites, etc. helpful after the baby arrived?

Anything not covered by the above questions that you'd like to convey?

Demographics:

Primary care taker

How long have you been breastfeeding or did you breastfeed

Relationship status

Number of children

Career or stay at home status

Age at first birth

Geographic location

Thanks so much…Kathleen

I've organized this book by question, so if there are particular areas of interest, you can read lots of thoughts and suggestions on other moms' experiences in that area. Not all moms answered all questions.

I'll start by introducing my contributors by their initials and some demographics:

AA is a 26-year-old, married mother of one. She is a stay-at-home mom and has been breastfeeding eight months. She lives in Maryland.

AB is a 37-year-old, married mom of one, who has been breastfeeding six weeks. She is currently "just pumping." She lives in Maryland.

AC is a 34-year-old, married mom of one. She's a stay-at-home, primary caretaker who has been breastfeeding for six months and is ready to slowly wean, so she can start working on baby #2. She lives in Maryland.

AD is a 34-year-old, married mother of two. She is currently working part time as an adjunct professor. She breastfed her first child for nine months and is currently breastfeeding her five-month-old. She recently moved from Massachusetts to Maryland.

AT is a 33-year-old, first-time mother, who has been "breastfeeding three months and counting." She's married, currently on leave from her job, and lives in Maryland.

BN is a 30-something, married mom of one child, living in the Maryland area. She returned to work when her child was three months old and is currently pumping.

BP is a 34-year-old mother of one in a committed relationship with a same sex partner. She is breastfeeding her one-year-old. She is currently working part-time outside the home and resides in Washington, DC.

BR is a 43-year-old, married, mother of twins. She works outside the home and has an au pair. She breastfed a total of one month. She lives in Maryland.

BW is a 31-year-old married mom, who shares primary caretaking with her husband. She had been breastfeeding her first baby five weeks when she filled out the questionnaire. She lives in Maryland.

CB is a 30-something mom currently breastfeeding her second child, a two-month-old baby. She lives in Maryland.

CK is a 35-year-old, married primary caretaker, who has been breastfeeding for five months and counting. As a full-time litigation attorney, she needs full-time daycare. She has help from her mother and mother-in-law, as well as daycare. She's currently trying to figure out how to stay home or work part-time. She resides in Maryland.

CV is a 29-year-old, married, stay-at-home mother of two. She breastfed her first child for nine months and is currently in the 11th month of breastfeeding her second. She lives in Maryland.

DA is a 33-year-old, married mom of one child, who lives in the Washington, DC, metro area. She is the primary caretaker of her four-month-old and just returned to work two weeks ago.

DG is a 31-year-old mom, who describes herself as "very happily married." She stayed at home with her baby for the first four months, dad stayed home one month, and then they employed a nanny. She has been breastfeeding nine months, but due to work-related travel is concerned her milk supply is getting depleted. She lives in Washington, DC.

DK is a 40-year-old, married mother of one. She works full time as a lobbyist and lives in Northern Virginia. She breastfed exclusively for the first three months, and then pumped until her baby was ten months old.

DS is a 27-year-old mom, who works part time. She's married and lives in Maryland. She's been breastfeeding her first child for 14 months.

EL is a 38-year-old, married mother of one. She was breastfeeding her two-month-old at the time of the questionnaire. She works part time from home. She lives in Maryland.

EM is a 27-year-old, married, primary caretaker of a six-month-old, who states she's "still going strong." She is currently staying at home with her first child. She lives in Maryland.

HA is a 36-year-old, married mother of one. She is the primary caretaker of her 4 ½-month-old baby, whom she is currently breastfeeding. She lives in Rockville, Maryland.

HA is a 30-something, married career mom of one child, who lives in Maryland.

HM is a 29-year-old, married, mother of three. She's currently a stay-at-home mom with what she describes as "sometimes-partial work" outside the home. She resides in Maryland and is currently breastfeeding twins.

JB is a 31-year-old, married mother of one. She works full time as a schoolteacher. She and her husband are primary caretakers, along with help from her mother-in-law and daycare. She is currently breastfeeding her four-month-old and lives in Maryland.

JD is a 35-year-old, married mother of one. She's in the process of returning to work and will use in-home daycare. She's been breastfeeding 11 weeks so far. She lives in Maryland.

JG is a 33-year-old, married, primary caretaker of one child. She was never able to breastfeed, but pumped her milk for just over 12 months. She works part-time at a children's museum near Boulder, Colorado.

JM is a 33-year-old primary caretaker of a two-year-old, who she breastfed for 14 months. She's a married homemaker and resides in Maryland.

JR is a 35-year-old married, career mom who utilizes daycare for her child. She's been breastfeeding 12 months and plans on continuing for a bit longer. She lives in Maryland.

KC is a 36-year-old, married mother of one. She works fulltime outside the home, while utilizing a nanny share. She is currently breastfeeding her two-month-old and resides in Maryland.

KF is a 36-year-old, married mom of one, who has been breastfeeding nine weeks so far. She lives in Maryland and will be returning to work soon.

KG is the primary caretaker of three children. She works at home and has been breastfeeding for "four plus years straight." She was 36 when her first child was born. She lives in Boulder, Colorado.

KK1 is a 31-year-old, who works full time. Her husband is the primary caretaker. She is currently breastfeeding her 11-month-old. She lives in Maryland.

KK2 is a 36-year-old, married mother of one, who breastfed (10%) and pumped for eight weeks. She is a business owner and career mom, who shares primary caretaking with a nanny. She resides somewhere in the Mid-Atlantic states.

KP is a 30-year-old, married mother of one who has been breastfeeding for 4½ months so far. Her goal is to breastfeed for the first year. She's an elementary school teacher in MD and is the primary care taker. She lives Maryland.

KS is a 40-year-old, married mom of one child. She works full time and is currently breastfeeding her 4½-month-old baby. She lives Maryland.

LG is a 29-year-old medical professional. Her husband is the primary caretaker. She breastfed for five days, but has been exclusively pumping for seven months. She lives in the Eastern part of the U.S.

LI is a 34-year-old, married, mom of one. She was on maternity leave for the first seven months, but now that she's working full time as a Project Manager, her child is in daycare. She's still breastfeeding at the one year plus mark. She resides in Maryland.

LK is a 38-year-old primary caretaker of two children. She's tandem nursing (meaning she continued to nurse her first child, who is now 14 months old, through her pregnancy and delivery of her now five week old second child). She has a female partner/wife. She worked part time until her second child was 3½ months, and then went full time. She lives in Maryland.

LT is a 39-year-old, married, professor of biology, currently staying home with her four-month-old. She will return to work later in the year. She lives in Maryland.

MF is a 33-year-old, married mother of two children. She has an eight-year-old and a six-month-old. She works full time at her career. She lives in Maryland.

MG is a 38-year-old, married, mother of twins. Since she works full time, she employs a nanny. She breastfed for seven weeks and currently lives in Canada.

MH is a 32-year-old attorney, who has a full-time nanny at home. She's been breastfeeding nine months and is going strong. She lives Maryland.

MK is a 31-year-old, married, telecommuting, working mother. She's been breastfeeding her baby for six months and states she's "trying to make it to at least a year!" She lives in Maryland.

MM is a 31-year-old mom, who is staying at home until she can find a new job. She's married and has been breastfeeding her first child for four months. She lives in Maryland.

OO is a 27-year-old, married, career mom, who is breastfeeding her three-month-old second child. She breastfed her first child for ten months. She utilizes dad, family members, and grannies for daycare. She resides in Maryland.

PB describes herself as a 30-year-old, married mom, sharing one-third of the responsibility for her first baby with her husband and her mom. She has a full-time career and breastfed her baby for a total of five weeks. She resides in Maryland.

RA is a 38-year-old, married mother of one. She's a career mom who plans on breastfeeding for the first year with the help of a good breastpump. She employs an au pair and states dad is very helpful on weekends and after work. She lives in Maryland.

RB is 38-year-old, married mom of one, who will return to work at six months. She is currently both breast and bottle (formula) feeding her baby. She lives Maryland.

RO is a 35-year-old, married mother of one. She states that she and her husband are both her baby's primary caregivers, but we work full time and she is in daycare every day. She has been breastfeeding for ten months and lives in Silver Spring, Maryland.

SE is the married mother of three children. She breastfed five months with her first, six months with her second, and four months with her third. She is a stay-at-home mom, who lives in Maryland. She is the primary caretaker.

SH is a 34-year-old mom, who is breastfeeding her two-month-old. She has recently returned to work. She lives in Maryland.

SI is a 35-year-old, married mother of one. She is currently a full-time litigation attorney, but is looking to figure out how to stay home or do part-time. Although she's the person her baby spends the most time with, the baby has two days with her maternal grandmother, one day with her paternal grandmother, and two days at daycare. She has breastfed for five months and counting. She resides in Maryland.

SK1 is a 31-year-old, elementary schoolteacher. She's married and has a two-month-old that she plans on breastfeeding for at least eight months. She lives in Maryland.

SK2 is a 38-year-old, married mom, who is working full time. She utilizes daycare Monday-Friday, although most days she telecommutes from home. She lives in Maryland.

SS is a 25-year-old, career mom, who is the primary caretaker. She's currently engaged and has been breastfeeding for four months. She plans "to breastfeed until her baby is 12 months old. (Will I make it until then…, who knows?)" She lives in Maryland.

TT1 is a 35-year-old, primary caretaker of her "partially breastfed" four-month-old. She describes herself as "happily married" and works part time as an engineer. She lives in Maryland.

TT2 is a 34-year-old, married mother of two. Both mother and father share primary caretaking. She breastfed her first child for four days, and then exclusively pumped for three months. With her second baby, she's currently combining breastfeeding (one to three times a day) and pumping (five to seven times a day). The baby is seven weeks right now (born 8/15/11). TT2 is a program manager at a federal agency and resides on the Eastern Coast of the USA in Maryland.

UG is a 33-year-old, married mother of one, who has a full-time career. She is currently breastfeeding her three-month-old. She lives in Maryland.

WC is a 37-year-old, married mother of one, who plans on returning to work full time when her six-week-old is a bit older. She lives in Maryland.

Part
1

Most Important Advice Before Birth and Prior to Breastfeeding

Question 1a. What's the most important bit of advice you wish you would have known prior to giving birth?

The women's answers centered mostly around the following subjects: bonding/emotional connectedness with baby, birth plans and the reality of giving birth, what a hospital stay is like following the birth, the first few weeks at home after delivery, breast feeding/breast pumps/Lactation Consultants, baby gear, and taking care of yourself. The responses are grouped by categories below.

Bonding/Emotional Connectedness with Baby

AB: Love at first sight does not always happen between a mother and her baby. It may not come the day after, or the day after that. It's ok and normal. How can you love someone you've only just met and you don't know?

EM: This might be stupid, but at first I thought the baby would immediately know and prefer me and that I'd be able to comfort her better than anyone else. Not so – at least not at first.

HM: You might not feel all warm and fuzzy love for your child right away. They are little, red, wrinkly aliens who come live with you, and cry and poop and need you every single minute. It's very hard, and you might be frightened by the fact that you don't feel "in love" right away. But you will. You just don't know them yet. And that takes time, sometimes more than you think it should. The love grows out of shared experiences over thousands of little moments. Families grow like plants – tiny sprouts, weak and vulnerable, tender. They need a lot of light, a lot of time, and beautiful music.

MK: Be prepared for your hormones to go a bit haywire after birth for a while. I expected to love my baby very much and to do everything in my power to take good care of her, but I had such strong protective feelings. After she was born, I had trouble being away from her long enough to shower!

RO: What I was definitely not prepared for was the intense separation anxiety I experienced after giving birth, which, of course, was related to my baby being in the NICU. I was a huge ball of weeping hormones for at least a day, and I had no idea what was going on or whether I would ever stop crying. This is not how you expect to feel after giving birth. And everyone kept assuring me that my baby would be fine, which was nice to hear, but not exactly the point.

Birth Plans and the Reality of Actually Giving Birth

CV: Birth plans are a waste of time. Don't get set on any part of labor or delivery going a certain way. I don't think a single thing from the two-page birth plan we made for our first child went my way. For my second child, my birth plan was one sentence: "Get the baby out."

DA: a) While in labor, it really is important to keep your wits about you. Those contractions during which I started to get upset when they came on were much worse than those I focused on breathing through.

b) Don't listen to doctors when they try to predict how much longer you'll be pregnant. It only makes each day at the end that much longer.

c) No one seems to talk about the shaking an epidural can cause, especially during a C-section. It isn't fun. I wish someone had told me it might happen!

DG: I had a pretty fast first labor, about six hours from first pain until delivery. And baby came at 37½ weeks. I was caught off guard at how fast it all happened. I'd been told average labor is 15 hours and heard lots and lots and lots of horror stories about labors lasting more than 24 hours. So that's what I was expecting. And with the due date – I just got that into my head as the DUE DATE. Not an estimated due date. I was planning to be at work until the due date and had plans for big meetings, a haircut, a pedicure, and lots of stuff that never happened, even though I was planning ahead. So I'd like to stress the importance of really being ready for the baby.

JD: You shouldn't have a pre-conceived idea of what the birth experience will be like, because whatever you imagine, it will be different.

JG: Ask a doula to be present at the birth! I had a preemie and ended up giving birth before I could attend a birthing class. I don't think I missed out on anything from the class, but I would have loved to have a doula present to help me as a comfort. Once I was in the delivery room, the doctor left and asked me to call him back when my water broke. A doula would have been a great comfort at that time, since I had no clue what was going to happen. My husband was in the room, but he had not given birth before either, so we were both in the dark as far as what to expect.

JR: Having a baby is like getting married. You can plan for it and register for things, but at the end of it all...your delivery might not go according to plan, and you will probably end up with things you find out you don't need from a registry.

It is great to have a birth plan, but be open to other options and learn about all of them. You never know how the delivery is going to go. It is great to take a class or just talk to as many people as possible to get a feel for the variety of deliveries people experienced and how they felt after the day was done.

KG: That it was going to be OK no matter how the birth turned out; I wasn't going to die. It would have made natural birth a lot easier.

27

KP: No matter how anxious and excited you are to get that baby out, let it come out when it is ready! Unless absolutely necessary, do not let the OB encourage an induction. Pitocin is the pits.

LT: No matter how many books I read or classes I took, etc., the baby didn't read the books or take the classes! He has, and always will have, a mind of his own! So you can only prepare so much for childbirth.

MM: You have little control over what happens during your pregnancy, childbirth, or post-partum period. Even if you ate healthy, exercised, and did everything the books tell you to do, sickness and the unexpected will and do happen. One must be flexible and keep an open mind (i.e., it may be in the best interest of the baby and the mother to go for the C-section, even though you had hoped and planned for a vaginal delivery). Being flexible and keeping an open mind helped me to avoid feeling 'guilty' or 'depressed.'

RO: Childbirth is not as big a deal as I thought it would be. Maybe this is because I had a relatively easy birth. But you spend so much time focusing and preparing for it, and it's really a pretty brief event compared to pregnancy and then parenting.

SK1: I felt well prepared by friends for this, and by hiring a doula. I highly recommend having a doula to reduce stress around birth. [My hospital's] nursing program has free ones (nursing students) if you call a week in advance of your due date.

TT1: The birth is just the beginning – it's not everything.

UG: It won't always go as you planned, and you should be prepared for that. If you stray from your birth plan, it doesn't matter in the end, as long as you have a healthy baby.

What a Hospital Stay is Like Following the Birth

BR: If you have a c-section, stay ahead of the pain by telling the nurse you are always on an eight and above in terms of pain, so they keep giving you the pain meds.

LK: After birth you bleed a lot a lot a lot for a long time. You will have painful cramps when your uterus contracts, especially when you nurse. These can last for days.

Childbirth class is pretty useless.

It is okay to let the nurses take your baby to the nursery, so you can sleep in the night – they'll bring the baby back to feed, and you need the sleep to prepare for going home and being on duty 24/7.

OO: Stay away from the hospital if you want to have a natural birth. Hospital employees like all sorts of interventions to avoid law suits, thus your chance to have a natural birth at a regular hospital is minimal.

PB: Don't count on any rest at the hospital!

SI: Don't be afraid to stand up for what you want. I told the anesthesiologist I did not want narcotics after my c-section because they made me sick, and she didn't believe/listen to me, so she gave me Percocet via IV, and it made me super sick. This sickness kept me from demanding as strenuously as I could that my daughter be kept with me. She and I were apart for about an hour after she was born.

SS: I wish I would have known to ask what to do in the event that your baby is not pooping or peeing when you take her home from hospital.

The First Few Weeks Home After Delivery

AA: I wish I had read some parenting books earlier and educated myself.

AT: The sleep deprivation can be exhausting for a mom who is EBF (exclusively breastfeeding) in the beginning.

BW: I took a birthing class and did some reading on the birthing process, so I knew what to expect and was well informed about giving birth. However, I was not aware of what would happen after the baby was born. I delivered naturally, without drugs/epidural, and the contractions and pushing were painful, but manageable.

I was prepared mentally for that, but I did not know that it'd be so painful when being sewn up and during the recovery. I really thought I'd rebound and be up and moving in no time, but it took a good three weeks before I could move around like a normal person again.

CB: People tell you to take naps when the baby does... DO THAT. Don't pick up around the house.

DS: So many things... I wish I knew how exhausting and overall-consuming it is to have a newborn, but no one can adequately prepare you for that before it happens.

EL: The first three months are boot camp. But you will sleep again...:)

EM: The first few weeks can be awful, but it gets so much better and easier.

JB: Recovery from labor takes time. Don't think you can bounce back in a week or two.

JM: Be prepared, especially if you've not known many babies. You will spend literally all your time and energy tending to this baby, at least for the immediate weeks following his/her birth. Make peace with this fact long prior to the due date.

JR: Take infant/child CPR.

KC: No matter how well organized or prepared you think you are, the very early stages of motherhood will likely overwhelm you. Know that this is normal and to be expected, and that the phase is very short-lived.

KF: Connect with lots of other moms. It's incredibly reassuring to know other people who really know what you're going through.

KK1: Don't get bogged down in details – pay attention to the big picture. It is so easy to worry yourself silly about the smallest things, especially when you're sleep deprived and not thinking as clearly as you might otherwise. Baby will not perish from eating the non-organic carrots and will probably be okay playing with a toy that the Oppenheim Toy Portfolio hasn't reviewed.

KS: Enjoy every minute of it. Time really flies by, and you look back and your baby is five months old. Be relaxed – your baby can sense how you are, so don't be stressed out.

KW: I wish I would have known to take each bit of advice that I received from other parents with a grain of salt.

Some new parents of small children have this sadistic urge to "advise" pregnant couples by sharing their most horrifying experiences under the guise of being helpful. They preface each bit of advice with "not to scare you, but...," and then, of course, they share one of their most difficult experiences/challenges from their own first few days. These stories usually involve incredibly long and painful deliveries, a baby who cries uncontrollably, and/or parental sleep deprivation.

What I've learned is that each experience is individual to the parent and the baby. And how you view your own situation and your attitude toward it can help or hinder how you cope with the challenging first few weeks and months after bringing home baby. So don't let those other parents freak you out! You and your baby will figure it out together, and it won't be as scary as all that...

LG: Have people designated to help you for at least the first two weeks. My husband and I came home trying to cook, clean, do chores, and take care of baby, and that was a big mistake. If I would have asked someone to prepare a meal plan sign up list with my close friends, that would have helped tremendously.

MF: When people said "get your sleep now because you're going to need it," they weren't kidding.

MH: Being a mother is one of the hardest jobs you will ever take on, but it is worth it. If you are used to working full time and juggling a ton of activities on top of working full time, you may think you can easily handle motherhood. You can, but it is a completely different challenge. While you are used to being in control of your life, your schedule, and things around you, you are no longer in complete control, no matter how much you plan and how many books you read.

RB: My sister had warned me that the first few weeks would be incredibly tough, and she was right. Luckily, she warned me before

31

I had my daughter, but no one had warned her, and she beat herself up about it for a while. She thought everyone had an easy time, and only learned later on how hard it is for most moms.

SE: Prepare to be totally unprepared! If this is your first baby, no matter how much you've read, no matter in what capacity you have worked with or cared for other people's children, no matter how many gadgets and gizmos you have purchased prior to the arrival of the baby, at times you will still feel anxious, overwhelmed, scared, incompetent, confused, frustrated, sad, angry, pissed off at your partner/spouse, totally alone, and totally on display, and it's OK! You will survive! Quit looking things up on the internet and comparing yourself to all the "other moms" out there. Trust in your instincts – they are stronger than you think they are. Consider yourself on sabbatical from your life and get your partner on board with this. Having a baby is not all rainbows and butterflies, but it is the most amazing thing you will do.

SK1:   Understand that the first month will feel crazy, but that it will end with you feeling wiser and calmer... or maybe two months :-)

TT1:   You really will get nothing non-baby related done after the baby comes.

WC: I didn't know my belly would be really squishy for weeks afterwards. I was used to having a firm prego belly, and then I was left with a jiggly belly.

       Also, I wish (and still wish) someone had told me how to recover from a c-section (suggested exercises, a way to gain muscle control – my abs were steel til the baby). Regarding c-sections, I only knew it was harder/longer to recover, but didn't know how to get back into shape after (and still don't – got no post-operative recovery exercises like one would with knee surgery or other major operation).

Breastfeeding/Breast Pumps/ Lactation Consultants

CK: I wish I had known how useful it would be to teach my baby to take the bottle. He had formula supplementation early on, but I stopped feeding him the bottle when my supply went up. Now I regret not having fed him a bottle of breastmilk on a regular basis, so that he would have gotten used to it. He now refuses the bottle, which makes it difficult for me to leave him with my husband or anyone else for longer than an hour or so.

HA: The breast pumps that are bought in the stores (e.g., Pump in Style) aren't very good.

JR: Do not buy a breast pump before the birth. If you want, you can do the research, but do not purchase the pump until you have the baby and know that he/she will breastfeed. You do not want to waste hundreds of dollars. Renting for the first month is great for supply and a good way to make sure you like pumping and the baby will breastfeed. It also costs less.

LK: Use the lactation consultants in the hospital (you may have to request one), even if you think you're doing okay at breastfeeding so far – you'll get great advice and it's the last time an LC will be free! Also, request to start pumping, that way you'll get pump parts billed to your insurance, and they can match the parts you'd need to buy for your home pump.

RA: MOST women require help from a lactation consultant (I think 80+ %), so I would understand that I REALLY should have taken a class ahead of time.

I thought that only women who had difficulty needed consultation. Because I usually figure out everything on my own, I thought this would be a "no brainer." My instinct got me going and my "brain" told me I was fine – until I was bleeding from my nipples….

TT2: You are not alone. Find support wherever you can. Visit a lactation consultant. There are so many products out there, and it's hard to know which products you'll really need. A good lactation consultant will know which products work well and also what's new on the market that major stores may not yet have picked up. Plus, buying products from the lactation consultant supports breastfeeding, not corporate greed.

Baby Gear

AC: Don't get caught up in all the baby crap to buy out there... less is more, really.

JD: You shouldn't buy stuff for more than a few steps ahead of where you are, and you shouldn't have a pre-conceived idea of what the birth experience will be like, because whatever you imagine, it will be different.

I bought tons of things like nursing bras, pads, etc. before I knew what I was doing and knew what my preferences were.

JR: Every baby is different, so return things you are not sure you will use from your registry. You can always repurchase it when you will need it. You do not want to have tons of loot that you will not use and are unable to return because the return period expired.

Taking Care of Yourself

KK2: There's likely a trite phrase, but I think someone, or multiple people, reminded me to be less stoic, perhaps be kind and gentle to myself, and do what I as mommy think is best. To trust my gut and not beat myself up if my gut goes against the grain.

MG: It is OK to take care of yourself (like a nap or a walk in fresh air) in the midst of trying to take care of babies!

SP: I wish someone had been able to convey to me just how all-consuming motherhood is. I had no idea that I would be "on." Or, to put it another way, I had no idea that it would be so difficult (and yet important) to retain time for myself... to make it a priority.

Kathy's Thoughts:

It's truly impossible to be as totally prepared as we'd like to be prior to our babies coming into this world.

I like the fact that no two women answered this question alike, although there was a theme of learning how to "roll with the punches." I believe that's an important lesson. I know it helps me when I lower my expectations, and then I'm not as disappointed when things don't turn out 100%.

Some moms do feel an instant bond with their babies – love at first sight, while others have a love and bond that develops over time. One of the important things to remember is that there is no one right way to do it or to have it happen to you.

My advice would be to keep your baby rooming in with you (at the hospital) as much as humanly possible. Optimally, you will not spend a lot of time by yourself in your room. Dads or partner, siblings, grandparents, and friends will be there to help.

I remember a funny (read... a little sad) story about a mother-baby couple I went to see at the hospital, right after she delivered her SIXTH child. Poor mom is laying there in bed, trying to rest, while one child is playing with the remote controls (raising and lowering the bed), another two were eating her food on her lunch tray, the fourth was sitting with her in bed complaining about something, and the fifth was turning on and off the water in the sink, and using up all the liquid soap. Dad was crashed-out on the couch, sound asleep, and the newborn was wide-eyed taking in all the commotion. I was happy she was able to laugh about it, but had asked her obstetrician if she could "please just go home."

It's important to try to pace yourself, sleeping when the baby sleeps and eating throughout the day when the opportunity arises. Don't be afraid to ask for what you want when you want it. People aren't always mind readers and simply don't know how to be helpful. It's ok to give them a gentle nudge.

Although narcotic pain meds should be taken when appropriate, try to switch to ibuprofen as soon as possible. This will prevent both your constipation and a very sleepy baby.

Remember there's a golden hour after the birth when it's the best time to initiate breastfeeding and lots of skin-to-skin contact. Ask the obstetrician if you can hold-off on the foot printing, weighing, bathing, and LoJack placement. (For those moms going to a hospital, there's sometimes a security band placed on the baby's ankle that sets off an alarm if the baby passes through an unauthorized doorway. This would, hopefully, prevent someone from stealing your baby.) I call it a LoJack because that's what I think it sounds like and because it makes parents laugh.

Also, some mothers have found that the pumps at the hospital are not compatible with the pumps the local lactation consultant rents (or that the same hospital rents). Check the brand and type, or you'll have spare parts you can't use when you get home. I agree that hospital grade pumps are far superior to help bring your milk in when baby is not latching or for any reason is not up to the task.

I absolutely agree to hold off on buying too many things prior to delivery. It's nice to see what you'll need, so you're not wasting time and money.

Doulas are invaluable. It's great to have someone there just for you, and only you, when you deliver. It can be difficult to think and talk when you're in pain, and your doula can be your advocate. Although dads are great resources, it's usually their first birth, too. I've never once heard a mom say she wishes she WOULDN'T have had a doula.

A bottle of expressed breastmilk a day, after the first couple weeks, can help babies be more flexible with feeding, so moms can leave them for awhile. The important thing is not to miss a day.

Postpartum supports can help your tummy feel less jiggly and vulnerable. You can also try a nice pair of Spanx. I think they're particularly helpful after a c-section, so you don't have to hold your tummy every time you cough.

Question 1b. What's the most important bit of advice you wish you would have known prior to breastfeeding?

The women had strong opinions about this question, which seemed to indicate that there has not been a lot of useful, practical, and supportive information about breastfeeding made readily available to new mothers. The expectations of nursing, the raw desire to nurse, and the emotional and physical toll it takes on a woman are also evident by these answers. The answers centered mostly around the following subjects: It is difficult (for virtually everyone), but it can get better; relaxing and being good to yourself; not breastfeeding (or not exclusively breastfeeding) is ok, too; latching issues; establishing and maintaining supply; using lactation consultants; educating yourself; pumping issues; and other words of wisdom that helped with the breastfeeding process.

It Is Difficult (for Virtually Everyone) But It Can Get Better...

AB: Breastfeeding is hard work – it's not natural or easy for every mother and every baby. Some babies take weeks to latch on. In those early days, a newborn baby may only suck a few times, then fall asleep, then suck a few more times and fall asleep again – this can continue for hours.

36

What your friends that have breastfed don't tell you is that (i) all of them have cried trying to nurse; (ii) they've tried everything (including putting ice packs on their baby's neck or back - I don't advocate doing this, to me it's torture) to keep their newborn awake while feeding; and (iii) many spend upwards of 18 to 20 hours a day in the first few weeks with a newborn attached to their breast.

If someone says that "breastfeeding is going well for them" or "they successfully breastfed," ask them what they mean. A good friend said that breastfeeding was successful. Shortly after, however, I learned that for nearly two weeks she cried every time she tried to breastfeed – her son always fell asleep, and they resorted to putting an ice pack on his bare back.

AC: It IS a lot of work – just because I pump ten ounces and my baby eats four ounces at a feeding, I still HAVE to nurse/pump on a schedule or I have major leaks and blockage!

BR: It takes up a lot of time and contributes to your feelings of isolation (my experience). I tried it for a month with twins, and then just gave up (and was perfectly fine with that).

CB: The first four weeks there's a lot of stress, crying, soreness… it takes a while to find your groove and figure things out.

CK: Almost all of the moms I've met have issues with breastfeeding in one way or another. Some had low milk supply (like me), and others have overabundance (which can lead to plugged ducts and mastitis). Almost all of us have dealt with nipple pain from a poor latch.

DG: What a time commitment it is. I had no idea. I had visions of spending maternity leave taking my baby out in public to parks, museums, shopping. I had no idea I'd have her attached to my boob every hour. It really [affects] your ability to have a life. I couldn't go out to eat with her, couldn't visit friends, couldn't take guests to the airport, couldn't do anything because I never knew when she'd want to eat again.

DS: It's a marathon. Every feeding was difficult at first. I found myself counting days until my son would reach four months and I could start adding solids to his diet because it was so exhausting. I didn't realize how emotionally taxing it would be (not to mention time-consuming – my baby would only nurse with a nipple shield after being released from the special care nursery at nine days old, which was an added hassle, and feedings lasted 40 minutes. One night during a 3:00 am feeding when I had nothing else to do, I added it up and realized I was spending nine hours a day nursing my son!) to provide such a wonderful gift to my child. I was convinced breastfeeding was best for me and my baby and was committed to it, but I had to take it one day (or even one feeding) at a time, and remind myself of the long-term goals, which has been a useful parenting skill in many ways. I tried to nurse without the nipple shield from time to time, but my baby just didn't know what to do with my breast. Then one day when he was ten weeks, we tried again, and he took to it like he'd never known anything else. Feedings became 20, and then ten minutes (I got half my life back!), and far less of a hassle. Although I'd always planned on weaning him at 12 months, he's now 14 months. We're taking our time in the process because breastfeeding has become a special thing for both of us. So hang in there – it does get better, and it is worth it.

EM: It is hard. It takes a lot of work. There are times that discomfort just happens and there is nothing wrong. You have to keep looking and looking until you can find someone GOOD to help with any problems. I went from thinking that breastfeeding wouldn't be painful at all (which is what I was told in the breastfeeding class at the local hospital) to thinking that normal breastfeeding must be extremely, blindingly painful (when we were initially told that our tongue-tied baby was nursing just fine), to seeing that it's probably more normal to be somewhere in the middle – some pain some of the time.

JD: It might be harder than you think. It's not always an intuitive process.

JR: Nursing gets easier, and it is only excruciatingly painful for the first week.

KC: Breastfeeding may be far more challenging than you're anticipating. Not enough is written on this topic. I read that it could be a little painful at first and about the cracking, etc.... but I never heard about the range of challenges women can face and how common those challenges have become. I assumed breastfeeding would be much easier and come much more naturally than it did. I had three friends who gave birth within months of me, and each faced similar challenges and was similarly surprised. Breastfeeding is something that seems like it should come so naturally – and yet it doesn't for some.

KG: It can be very difficult, it's common to have problems, and it's OK to seek help.

KK1: I wish someone would have warned me how hard those early days really are – and that it gets SO MUCH easier if you'll just push through those hard times.

KK2: I wish I'd known it could be very challenging.

LK: It gets easier.

SE: It rarely goes really well for anyone. It is a learning experience and can be very exhausting. It can be incredibly intense. You may feel like it has consumed your entire life in the very beginning because it does. There is light at the end of the tunnel.

TT1: It's harder than I could imagine and we took a breastfeeding class. It's not an all or nothing thing.

UG: It won't always come naturally. It will take work and be frustrating at times, but stick with it and be patient.

Relax, Be Good to Yourself...

HM: The entire fate of Western civilization does not rest on you being a "success" at breastfeeding. There are no grades. There are no report cards. In a year, they'll be eating food, and all that pressure you put on yourself will seem silly. But it's real, and you have to recognize it. Take deep breaths. Drink a ton of water. Ask people for help. Let other people do the things you don't want to do (like dishes and laundry) and just be with your baby. Or don't for a while if that's what you need. But don't feel like you need to win an award at breastfeeding because you won't. The amount you succeed is no measure of your love for your child. Relax.

JB: Don't get [super] stressed if it doesn't always go the way you think it will.

LT: How much my mood/emotions/feelings/stress would affect my milk supply! Right before going back to work I got very stressed out, and then I found I couldn't let down.

MF: Even though breastfeeding is natural, it is a learned process and doesn't happen overnight.

Not Breastfeeding (Or Not Exclusively Breastfeeding) Is OK, Too...

AB: If breastfeeding doesn't work for you, don't feel guilty or feel bad.

DA: There is no bonding when you and the baby are both in tears.

EL: Giving bottles and formula is not always the end of the world – your baby might just hang in there and go back to the breast.

KC: I wanted to breastfeed very badly. I felt guilty about all of the difficulties I was having and, ultimately, my decision to stop breastfeeding. It was the best decision for us at the time, but a very difficult one to make given the societal (and my own self-imposed) pressure to continue.

KK2: While breast is best, something is better than nothing, and nothing can replace bonding with baby!

LK: Formula isn't rat poison. A happy mom is better than a breastfeeding mom who is miserable.

MG: You are not a terrible failure if it doesn't work.

SE: If you feel like you are totally [losing] yourself, if you are depressed and anxious and spending most of your days crying and frustrated, seek help and know that it is okay to stop. Be reasonable with yourself. Give yourself the same advice you would give someone else. Think about all the really important people in your life. Do you know if they were breastfed? Do you care?

TT1: Lots of people use both formula and breastmilk.

I wonder how on earth did humanity survive if our survival was dependent on breastfeeding???

Latching On...

AB: Not all babies are natural latchers (whatever it means to be a natural latcher).

CV: Watch online videos of women learning to nurse newborns, or even better, if you have a close friend with a newborn or infant, watch her. I don't care how many breastfeeding classes you take with baby dolls or how many charts you look at regarding how it works, you've got to see it in action and see someone else troubleshooting "latching on."

JR: The hospital tells you nothing. It is very helpful to your desire to breastfeed if you are able to start trying soon after delivery. No one is going to come in and say now let's try to latch your baby.

PB: There are often issues with latching.

SP: Get help early. After making it through a marathon natural labor, my idea of the pain scale had been radically transformed (or smashed to pieces). I was in a great deal of pain from the nursing, but thought, "Oh, this is nothing compared with labor! This must just be the normal amount of discomfort they say comes with nursing!" When I finally went to a lactation consultant, she actually gasped when she saw my nipples. She said she'd never seen anything so bad! (In hindsight, probably not the most encouraging words... but in a way, it was nice to know that I wasn't crazy or making a mountain out of a molehill.)

SS: How to properly latch the baby on the breast. My local hospital gave me horrible instructions.

TT2: I wish someone had told me that it was going to hurt – a lot. And that if I can get through the first three weeks, things will get much better/easier. And how to care for sore nipples during those first few weeks.

BW: I would have liked to have known that it requires a lot of time to get the milk levels established. I didn't realize that I needed to breastfeed/pump every two to three hours for the first few weeks.

HA: My regret was that during the growth spurt I thought I could not provide enough milk, so I switched to formula for two weeks (until Kathy told me not to use it anymore). If I had known about the important time frame (40 days post birth) for building my milk supply, I would have had more confidence to stick with it.

KK2: I wish I had been told earlier, especially if pumping doesn't work out to increase milk production, that bringing the baby to the breast and body skin-to-skin in lieu of the stressful pumping would help.

KP: No matter how tired you are, nurse as often as possible for the first few weeks. Keep that baby at the breast and do not unlatch him. The first few weeks are so important in building your supply.

MK: I've had some trouble with milk supply while breastfeeding. I knew how important latch was and all about the need to breastfeed frequently in the beginning, but I had no idea that milk supply could be an issue. I wish I would have known that, while the frequency of breastfeeding in the early days IS very important, it is also very important to empty your breasts when you breastfeed in order to help establish a good supply.

PB: There are often issues [with the] amount of production.

RB: What I didn't know was how important those first few weeks are to establishing your milk supply, what factors can make it harder to get your milk supply up and running, and what to do about it. In the hospital I saw three different lactation consultants who all told me to do different things, but I didn't start pumping until my daughter was a month old. If I had started doing the things [Kathy] suggested earlier, I think that could have helped my supply be better than it is.

WC: It can take a few days for the milk to come in. I gave birth at 1:00 am on Thursday morning and my milk didn't come in until

Monday morning. I wish I had supplemented with formula in the first few days.

Using Lactation Consultants...

AA: Don't be scared to get help if you don't get it right.

CK: So the best advice I could have gotten was to line up a lactation consultant before the birth and expect to turn to her for lots of advice all through the nursing relationship.

DA: If you're really wanting to breastfeed, I recommend having a lactation consultant examine your breasts before your baby is born. If I had known beforehand that my nipples were going to cause some issues for me, I could have had a better approach and not spent so much time frustrated and upset.

JM: Get in touch with a lactation specialist BEFORE the baby is born. Paging through books is very helpful, sure, but having someone hands on to walk you through the process is way, way better... especially in the first days after the baby is born.

OO: Insist on seeing a breastfeeding consultant before you leave the hospital. It is not as easy a task to breastfeed as some may think.

SK1:   Find a great lactation consultant who will help you feel normal and that you trust to give you options to make things easier!

Educating Yourself...

JR: Classes and the *Nursing Mother's Companion* by Kathleen Huggins is a great quick reference. Read it before you deliver.

KF: Connect with lots of other moms/professionals to support you in your breastfeeding endeavors. I really didn't think I'd need any help, and I ended up needing a lot of help, reassurance, and support.

KW: Take a class! Read a book! Educate yourself! I personally spent so much time worrying about my delivery that I only skimmed the information I had on breastfeeding... And the basic child-birthing

43

class that I did take only touched on the basics of breastfeeding, which didn't cut it when I was struggling with breastfeeding in the hospital and in the early days after coming home... Prepare yourself for breastfeeding. I've personally found it to be one of my biggest challenges. But again – that's just me.

RA: Pain is NOT normal during the entire process. I'd heard that it hurts (more so than child birth), so when I was in excruciating pain, I thought "Aha! I've got it! I'm succeeding! In a couple weeks it won't hurt. OUCH!!!" Again, had I taken a breastfeeding class or met with a consultant I'd have been aware in the first day that I needed assistance (rather than day four bleeding and needing to switch to formula in the hospital for her weight to go up, thereby putting my milk supply at risk).

Pumping...

BN: It may seem obvious, but I wish I knew that I should start pumping right away after every feeding. I thought I would pump to create a stash of breastmilk for when I went back to work. I did not realize that pumping helped produce more milk. The thought of pumping intimidated me and overwhelmed me. So much of my day as a new mom was spent breastfeeding, I could not imagine pumping in between feeding sessions. I wish now I had pumped after every feeding to help make more milk.

DK: More information about pumping – specifically how to start pumping early on and how to time it to ensure he was still getting enough when he nursed. One of the lactation specialists who I did ask, did not encourage pumping – telling me I could wait until a couple of weeks before I went back to work.

EL: If your milk does not come in/baby loses too much weight over the first few days, leave the hospital with a *hospital-grade pump* at the get go.

JB: Pump from the start. Create a stockpile in the freezer, especially if you're going back to work.

KS: Make sure you have a good pump.

44

LK: Hospital-grade pumps make a world of difference – it is worth renting one after birth.

MM: Hospital-grade pumps are easy to rent and help to stimulate milk flow when you're having trouble producing milk. I also wish someone told me to pump around the clock during my days in the hospital to help with the feeding.

Other Words of Wisdom That Helped With the Breastfeeding Process...

AC: Being fully committed to breastfeeding is the best advice.

AT: The feedings will become less frequent over time.

DA: Talk to your partner before the baby is born about how committed you're feeling about breastfeeding. Tell him/her how to encourage you and to what end.

EL: Go on <u>Domperidone</u> in the first few weeks. With no side effects, you have nothing to lose. And you must have the right nipple cream – without that, I was useless.

KK1: I wish someone had warned me away from buying a breastfeeding pillow until I knew what I really needed. Who has the time or energy to wrap and snap a My Breast Friend around herself in the middle of the night?

LG: You do not need to breastfeed for more than ten minutes on each side the first two, or a few more, days of life. I breastfed for 40 minutes on each side starting day one and my nipples only lasted five days! My baby was falling asleep, latching off, after ten minutes, and I was perplexed thinking, "What is wrong with her? Why does she fall asleep?"

LK: If you have big boobs, wear a bra 24-7.

LT: How attached I would get to nursing and how difficult it would be to give it up.

MH: While breastfeeding is a natural process, it does not come naturally to every mom and baby combo. If you think you are having

45

trouble, get help immediately. Many women and books say that it is normal for breastfeeding to hurt. That is NOT ACCURATE. It is normal for it to feel uncomfortable or different. If you are experiencing pain, holding tears back, dreading feeding time or bleeding, you need help. It's okay to ask for it!

MM: It takes a few extra days for the milk to come in when you have a c-section.

RO: What I wish someone had told me before breastfeeding was how freaky it would be when my milk came in. No one really talks about that except for some vague references to relieving engorgement. I felt like I had aliens exploding out of my chest, and no matter how many times I demanded that my mother tell me when this would end, she refused to give me a good answer. Really, someone should tell new moms what that's going to be like and that it will only last a couple of days.

SH: Surprisingly, I've found that a lot of people are NOT supportive of breastfeeding. If it's what you want to do, don't let others discourage you.

SI: Boobs are like children and require structure and predictability. Big boobs do not necessarily equal easy breastfeeding.

SK2: There are many ways to supplement and facilitate breastfeeding. To breastfeed exclusively be prepared to do so every two hours for the first couple months, at minimum. Try to get a nurse in when breastfeeding at first during the night to ensure baby is latched on to the proper part of the breast. You may be too tired/medicated to feel if the baby is not even on the nipple. Feeding plans, like birth plans, can very quickly need large adjustments.

Kathy's Thoughts:

All good information. Here are a few thoughts of my own. If I had been able to give these moms some advice when they were having problems, I might have been able to help.

- Regarding low milk supply, an interesting fact is moms who drink more water than what they're thirsty for, actually will make less milk. I know it's counter-intuitive, but it's true.

- Empty breasts make milk.

- Not ALL c-section moms take extra days to bring in their milk.

- Although it's always an option to use some formula with breastfeeding, I'd caution moms that this will definitely decrease their supply and is the beginning of weaning. It can also be very hard on the baby's digestive system since formula is recognized as more of a solid food. Most moms find they can make enough milk to feed their babies, if that's their intention.

- There are lots of ways to help rouse a sleepy baby: keep yourselves skin-to-skin, rub the baby's shoulder, rub the feet, massage from the palms toward the baby's armpits and from the feet to the groin, breast compressions, or walk up the baby's back with your fingers (starting at the base and working up the neck). Take the baby off the breast and switch to the other side, with a burping session in between.

- Have confidence in yourself and your breasts!

- Lactation consultants do what they do best when you work with them! If possible, have one come to your home.

Most Helpful with Breastfeeding

Question 2: What one thing helps more moms succeed at breastfeeding?

The women's responses centered around getting support from others, getting a lactation consultant, knowing that getting the hang of breastfeeding takes time, knowing the ins and outs of pumping/ supplementing, being good to yourself and caring for yourself, and other helpful advice.

Support From Others...

AB: Support of your spouse/partner.

BN: Talking with girlfriends who have been successful. Hearing success stories really provided a light at the end of the tunnel and helped calm [my] anxieties (of which I have many).

BW: It wasn't until I talked to some new mothers during my pregnancy that I learned that breastfeeding can be hard and even painful. Beforehand, I thought it would be natural and easy. After talking to the new mothers, I was motivated to attend a class and read a book about it.

CV: Talk to other moms who have been through it while you're in the throws of it. It is inevitable that you will think, "I can't do this anymore. I have a leech. What have I become? This baby wants to eat 20 out of 24 hours!" Having friends who can tell you that you will come out the other side is what got me through it.

DA: A supportive pediatrician.

DS: Support from other moms. My husband was very supportive of my decision to breastfeed, even though we had a hard beginning, but I'm not sure I would have made it without the weekly breastfeeding group at our local hospital, where lactation consultants answered questions or simply gave encouragement. I also met other moms with kids the same age who became a key source of support and encouragement not just for breastfeeding, but for sleeping, diapering, child development, and my own sanity.

EM: Just keep looking until you can find someone who can really help with problems. Sometimes the pediatrician, your doctor, the nurses at the hospital, etc. may not be able to help with really specific problems.

HM: Talk, tell people how you feel, and ask for help.

JM: Supportive spouse/partner/family member. While I breastfed from our bed, my husband stayed on hand to burp the baby, help clean up his spit-up, change diapers mid-feeding session, and offer LOTS of encouragement. He also was the keeper of a clean pair of socks, for me to bite down on when the pain of breastfeeding our tongue-tied child was too much to bear.

KF: Support and reassurance. No gadget or book helped me more than people telling me that I was doing a good job and just needed to stick with it.

KP: Build your support group before baby. You need to be comfortable with breastfeeding before others around you will be. And you need to have others around you be supportive of breastfeeding for it to work.

KS: Support from the husband in helping out, so you are relaxed.

LG: Definitely, I could not have done it without the support from my husband. I was ready to quit and he pushed me, literally, got me to continue.

MH: A group of moms/support group of women that breastfeed and can help.

MK: Support!

RO: I had support from my mom who breastfed, and two good friends who were very committed to breastfeeding as working moms. Everyone should have someone to talk to on a regular basis about the joys, challenges, and just the process of nursing.

SE: Support Support Support!

SK2: Talking to other moms like you.

SS: Support from their partner!

Lactation Consultant...

AB: A great (not good, but great) lactation consultant.

AC: Talk to a lactation consultant right after giving birth, even if nursing is going well. They can prepare you for the glitches that can and WILL happen.

AT: Don't be afraid to ask for help early, rather than giving up.

DA: A great lactation consultant.

DS: A good lactation consultant.

HM: You should NOT be in horrible pain. Yes, it can be uncomfortable at first, but there is a difference between "sweet discomfort" and real, excruciating pain. Don't feel like you are helping anyone to "tough it out." Get help. Get treated. You can feel better – your body, your mind, and your baby will thank you. Well, your baby won't thank you. But they do appreciate it!

JD: A good lactation consultant. No, really :)

JR: An identified lactation consultant or other support person that can help you with the breastfeeding process within the first 24-36 hours. Do not wait for there to be a major problem, check to make sure you are on track before too much time passes. If you are not, then it is harder to get you and your baby in sync.

KC: Seek out a qualified, patient lactation consultant.

KK1: Visit a lactation consultant as soon as possible! I know for a fact that I would not be breastfeeding right now if I hadn't.

LK: Get a lactation consultant at the first sign of trouble.

LT: Having access to an excellent, resourceful, and friendly lactation consultant who is available via a variety of means (email, phone, in person). Kathy – your willingness to respond to my sometimes very crazy emails made it incredibly easy to get good advice about breastfeeding very quickly!

MF: A great lactation consultant will be your best friend. :)

MK: There is nothing that has helped me more than having a caring and knowledgeable lactation consultant available to answer my questions and help me deal with problems that arise.

OO: Seeing a lactation consultant helped me immensely.

RA: Accept a lactation consultant's help by taking a breastfeeding class BEFORE birth and having them check in on you for at least 30 minutes in the first day after birth to be sure you're doing it right, so you correct things before you have any issues.

RB: Obviously, having a lactation consultant to give advice, so you don't flounder too much, is incredibly helpful.

RO: And at the start, when I was trying to feed a five pound baby, it was crucial that I got good advice from Kathy. I would have never known that I needed to pump to get my milk supply established if I hadn't had you to advise me.

SE: Get a good recommendation for a lactation consultant before you give birth. Have the number on hand and ready to go.

SI: Having a lactation consultant who was willing to respond to my middle of the night breastfeeding quandaries and not push an agenda.

SK2: USE the lactation consultants on staff at your hospital during your stay as much as possible and also at your pediatrician's office. Ask for help, that's what they're there for!

It Takes Time

AA: Breastfeeding is a huge commitment. It takes lot of patience.

BW: The one thing that would help moms succeed is just knowing that breastfeeding isn't always as easy and intuitive as you'd think. It takes time and patience.

DA: Patience.

EM: Also issues can take a very long time to resolve, but it doesn't mean they won't resolve. We've been breastfeeding fine since my daughter's tongue-tie got fixed three months ago, but I still see improvement and have had some level of pain that improves little by little even now.

KG: Knowing how much easier (meaning breastfeeding is more convenient and cheaper and helps you get more sleep) it is after the first hurdles.

KW: Knowing that you DO have the milk in there – be confident. It just takes time, patience, and practice in getting to know your own breasts, your baby's ability to latch and suck properly, and your milk supply to regulate itself to the needs of your child. You WILL figure it out TOGETHER - WITH TIME.

MM: Your nipples will not stay sore forever. It does get better.

PB: Patience.

RB: Reassurance that it is difficult for most moms and that time will help. For me, things turned around at six weeks – less pain, less stress, etc.

Pumping/Supplementing

EL: Pump, pump and pump. [It] increases milk supply and gives you flexibility.

HA: Regarding the pumping time, our pediatrician said ten minutes was enough, but actually to get your body to produce more milk, you have to keep pumping for a while after your flow stops.

JG: I was successful at pumping because I had designated places (at home, at work, and at the hospital) and times for pumping throughout the day. I carried the pump with me everywhere I went. It made it very easy to pump regularly.

LK: Rent a hospital grade pump. Don't worry too much about how much you pump.

SE: Know where you need to go for pump rentals, and try and learn something about how they work – and know what the cost is so you don't have sticker shock.

SK2: If you can get the baby to ALSO take expressed breastmilk or formula from a bottle, you will have much more freedom and flexibility, and perhaps enjoy breastfeeding even more.

TT2: A breastpump. When I asked the hospital lactation consultant about renting a breast pump, she told me I should wait at least three or four weeks before giving the baby a bottle and that was it – nothing more. Since I had problems breastfeeding my first child because she was tongue-tied, I knew the virtues of a breast pump, so I had my husband go to the store while I was at the hospital to buy me a breast pump. A breast pump gives the mother freedom. Freedom to rest one's nipples to allow them to heal. Freedom to sleep. Freedom to leave the house for a couple of hours without the baby without worrying whether the baby is hungry.

Be Good to Yourself and Take Care of Yourself

CK: Don't blame yourself for not having enough milk.

HA: At first I thought I wasn't providing enough milk, but I kept trying and discovered that actually, I was doing a good job.

HM: Drink TONS of water and do your best to sleep when the baby sleeps. The rest will help you relax and think clearly – which all helps with the flow of energy and happiness and milk!

JB: Try different methods and find a way that works best for you. Don't stress!

KC: If you're having difficulties, try to relax, and don't be so hard on yourself. Those first few weeks can be stressful and overwhelming. Putting added pressure on yourself won't make the process any easier or increase your likelihood of success.

KK2: To be aware of ALL the resources available free and also paid to help you succeed; but in the end, to be kind to themselves throughout the process.

MG: Not feeling guilty.

SP: I wish there were more widespread wisdom about postpartum nutrition. One of the reasons I believe I succeeded with breastfeeding and was able to exclusively breastfeed twins until we introduced solids at six to seven months, was that I paid very close attention to consuming nutrient dense foods. I took fish oil capsules and raw liver capsules, and ate like I was still pregnant with twins, frankly... more like five meals a day instead of three. I don't mean for women to just eat excessively, but I believe it's important for nursing moms to not start dieting as soon as the baby is born. I also would stir a teaspoon of coconut oil into my tea each morning, which I did to get more of the good lauric acid into my breastmilk.

TT1: Redefine success. Be flexible with what success means.

Other Things That Helped

AA: Love and affection for your baby.

BR: Have only one child?

CB: The nipple sandwich on fresh, NOT STALE, bread! It took me until my second kid to understand the importance of this, and now I have SO much more confidence because I am not in PAIN!

DG: Buy the right clothes. I spent so much time during the pregnancy worrying about what I would need for baby and absolutely no time thinking about what I would need for me. I had no idea I would need things like nursing bras and shirts. And then when you nurse for a year, you need a lot of nursing bras and shirts. I had a whole summer wardrobe that I wasn't able to wear because it was a lot of sun dresses that didn't allow me to get my boobs out. There are lots of suggestions that I think would help moms with breastfeeding – I heard a lot of them myself. But no one ever told me to think about clothing.

KP: Once baby is here, get out and nurse in public. Figure out places you can nurse comfortably and places to stay away from. Soon enough you will be comfortable nursing anywhere and will be able to do it discreetly enough no one will even notice what you are doing under there!

KS: A quiet place to nurse. Also, proper positioning with a pillow so as not to hurt your neck or back by hunching over all the time. Making sure you have all the supplies for a pump and storing milk.

JR: Trying immediately [and] having some background instruction from a book or class.

MH: "My breast friend" pillow was invaluable. Don't be ashamed or afraid to take it with you when you go out to make breastfeeding out/in public easier.

SK1: Different position options are nice.

SK2: Find position(s) that's right for you and baby, not necessarily textbook correct.

Kathy's Thoughts:

When pumping, watch for your letdowns (meaning when the milk starts to come out like a little showerhead). Four letdowns will equal more than 100% out of your breasts. What this means is that by the time your milk lets down during the fourth time, you are expressing milk that you started making at the beginning of the pumping session. This might take about 30 minutes or slightly more.

Suggestions/Advice to Benefit a New Mom

Question 3. Any other suggestions or advice that would benefit a new mom?

AA: Moms should be selfless and have tons of patience.

AB: Whenever I was asked during my pregnancy whether I would breastfeed, my standard response was "I'd like to if we can." Don't make promises to yourself that you may not be able to keep – wait and see how things go for you and your baby. Parenthood is hard enough. Breastfeeding is that much harder, and there is no shame in making a decision once you have all the information.

AC: I was thinking more about this and had a few additional thoughts:

1. I am a girly girl and tend to wear a lot of scents... like body lotion, perfume, or body spray, etc. This was really hard on the twins when nursing, but it wasn't clear to me until I realized later in the day (when it had worn off), they nursed better than in the morning (which is when I would get a shower and slather myself in scents). So long story being – I would advise new moms to switch to Dove or something GENTLE, and not to use perfume, as this was negatively impacting our progress, but was unclear to me.

2. The types of bras drastically impacted my production. Underwire – BAD... no wire – GOOD! Again happened by switching to nursing tank tops, but did not realize what a difference it made.

3. If pumping: bottles – Avent – enough said... can't speak highly enough about them, less parts, good range of flow for varying ages, including preemies.

When to clean and how to clean tubing – I steamed it in these Medela bags that THEY recommend for sanitizing, and it melted the plastic three times!!! Finally switched to soaking in bleach/ water solution (same as ratio to clean toys, etc.) once every other day, also had a spare part of ALL accessories.

Do not buy car chargers!! Go to Home Depot, and for $15, they sell a small little box that you can plug any household item into with a car adapter on the other end. Same price as the car charger AND you can reuse.

AC: Pump, pump, pump.

AT: Have meals prepared and frozen before the birth.

BN: There is a great blog on the net called "The Longest Shortest Time" about being a new mom. The title is truly what it is like having a newborn. It is the longest shortest time, so when it feels super long, just know it will be over before you know it.

BP: When I was pregnant, breastfeeding was one of the things I looked forward to the most, and I assumed that it would be as natural for me as breathing. So I was surprised by my uncertainty and by the challenges I encountered when I first started nursing my son Henry. I wasn't sure how to position myself, and his body felt unfamiliar in my hands. My breasts felt strange and unfamiliar, as well. I would awkwardly lift him to my chest, and fumble to bring his mouth to the nipple. I felt so unsure of myself. In those first days after my son was born, he would often grasp for the nipple with his mouth, only to stiffen, fall off the breast, and cry in frustration. I would look down into his sobbing (and empty) mouth, and feel completely incompetent and helpless. He needed to eat, and I urgently wanted to feed him, but I had no idea how to make things work better. I was hard on myself; I felt as though I had failed some basic parenting test – I couldn't even nurse my son successfully! On some level, I knew that other women struggled, too, and that breastfeeding challenges were common, but I was also ashamed; I felt as though I should be able to do it.

Asking for help with breastfeeding was difficult for me. I even had trouble accepting suggestions from my partner, as she read breastfeeding guides and tried to help me position Henry. She wanted to help, but I felt as though she couldn't understand that it was much harder than it looked. I worried about admitting that I was having trouble. Ultimately, when I did get support, things improved, and I began to appreciate that nursing was an art, and that it took practice. Henry and I both needed to get to know each other, and to learn each other's gestures and signals. Because it was new, there were some false starts and mistakes, but staying with it, despite the frustration, and accepting support enabled Henry and I to get better at breastfeeding, and over the first few weeks it became a really satisfying experience of bonding for us.

BR: Get ready to be tired all the time until they're 18 probably, and prepare for memory loss, so write everything down. Also, a family network is very helpful for additional help and just some free time for you and your partner that won't add $30+ to the bill for your night out. If you have someone to take your child for the night occasionally, that is the best (we don't, but my sister does, and I envy that!).

Prepare for weekends to be the hardest since you have the child/ren all the time. I thought on some level I'd have weekends to 'recover' from the week (I work full time), but now my husband and I actually look forward to Mondays, so that we can get a break at work.

If you have twins, make sure to get them on the same schedule ASAP (if you feed one, wake up the other one and feed that one, too, etc.).

BW: - Seeking help isn't a sign of failure.

- Let your husband help – I know I couldn't have figured it out as quickly or as well without mine!

CB: Definitely visit a lactation specialist... They say it's not supposed to hurt and what can be so hard about a baby sucking your nipple?

But it's hard if no one teaches you how to do it! And you probably won't get it right the first or second time!

CK: Babies are more resilient than they look. So don't blame yourself if things don't happen the way you expect. Cut yourself a break and remember, years ago, mommies smoke and drank and somehow we all turned out fine.

CV: Find a lactation consultant you can turn to before you have the baby and use the consultant services at your hospital or birthing center, even if everything is going swimmingly. You'll get free stuff (like soothing gel pads and nipple cream), and it can only help. Finding a lactation consultant before birth if you're committed to nursing is as important as finding a pediatrician ahead of time.

DA: The word "natural" gets thrown around a lot in referring to breastfeeding, which makes any new mom struggling with it feel somehow "unnatural" or wrong. I wish people would stop using the word "natural" because for some of us it feels anything BUT! It doesn't come easy for many women and the pressure can be enormous.

Remember a lot of other women look to you in order to make themselves feel good about whatever decision *they* made (did they breastfeed, did they formula feed, did they pump at work, did they not) and so may try to pressure you to make one decision or another because if you follow what they did, it'll give them a good feeling about whatever they did. Try to block that all out. You have to do what's in YOUR heart.

DG: I took a breastfeeding class offered at the hospital, which was very helpful, so I'd recommend that for all new moms. But I think there should be more time spent on the various positions. It was presented as if the cradle hold is the easiest, so don't even try anything else. But once I "learned" how to breastfeed while lying down, it changed my life. Why didn't they focus on that in the class? You're constantly exhausted and tired – and I certainly had some breastfeeding sessions where I fell asleep lying down and woke up three hours later. But baby was sleeping too, so it was wonderful!

DK: Many thanks for the main messages from your first book, *Start Here*. I totally agree with you, and I thought I was old fashioned. I could never leave my son behind with a nanny, and one day when I left to see the doctor, I was horrified when I came back.

I went to the doctor and she probably thought that I had gone to the office for some meeting (I have worked remotely since my son was born, but go for meetings, etc.). When I returned I heard my son crying. I waited to see her reaction and was shocked that she was shouting at him and abusing him. Every other word in her sentence was an abuse. I was shaking and I froze... My husband was in India, then, and I didn't want to react in anger. So, I just waited calmly for him to return and fired her the Saturday after bearing her for four days... She seemed extremely nice and loving towards my son... always caring like my mom used to... so it was very shocking. I also could not understand her anger and frustration... it had been only an hour since my baby got up (I returned in an hour, and he got up just before I left). I fired her, even though I didn't have an alternative then...

Not all nannies are this way, but I cannot trust a nanny/day care anymore... at least 'till my baby can speak up.

After talking to you and reading the excerpt from your book, I am happy that I am old fashioned.

DK: What a friend told me – that people have been doing this for thousands of years. Don't sweat everything.

DS: Get out! Your world will probably shrink when you have a baby, and for a week or two that's fine. But when I first went to the breastfeeding support group at the hospital, I realized how small my world had become – it basically consisted of nursing on the couch and nursing in the bed, with occasional ventures to the kitchen or bathroom. Getting out of the house reminded me that the world did not consist of breastfeeding on demand and that I had a life outside of nursing my child. If you can get out without the baby, even if it's just to go to the doctor's office or the grocery store, all the better. But heading over to another mom's house with the baby in tow can be life-giving and encouraging in more ways than you will realize.

Let people help. Even your mother-in-law. Don't feel like you have to do everything because you're the mom – there's nothing your husband, mom, or helper can't do except breastfeed. So make a grocery list for them, or let them sweep the floor, or ask them to give the baby a bath and diaper change.

Remember, "this too shall pass." And that goes for the stages you love, as well as the ones that can't end quickly enough. Everything with a baby is temporary; be careful not to spend the first years of your little one's life wishing them away for a time when things will be easier (besides, it doesn't get easier; the challenges just change content). "The days are long, but the years are short."

There's way too much information out there for your own good. Don't read every book, check every website, or ask everyone you know for information; you'll be inundated, overwhelmed, and likely too paralyzed by fear and conflicting opinions to make a decision. Check out a few sources, pick and choose what works for you and your family, and don't feel bad about leaving the rest by the wayside. People have been having babies for millennia, and most of them have survived with or without the landslide of modern theories about child-raising.

You can (and probably will) second-guess every decision you make. And not just major ones like, "Does my child need to go to the ER for this?" either. I would practically pull my hair when my infant son wouldn't settle down for naps, wondering whether I put him down too early or too late, whether I spent too long in the pre-sleep routine or needed to change something in it, whether I was a failure as a mom because I couldn't get my child to sleep . . . it sounds crazy, but there's no manual for infants or troubleshooting guide for your particular baby, and it's natural to wonder if you're doing it right. Take a deep breath, remind yourself that babies are resilient, and keep forging ahead.

"Blue is bad; pink is prime." I volunteer as an EMT (or at least I did before my child sucked up all my free time and then some), and that's one of the key phrases in caring for patients. If [his or her] skin is pink, it means their breathing and their circulation are in working order. It's amazing what you forget or don't believe as a new parent, though; our son spent his first eight days in the Special Care Nursery hooked up to monitors that told us every time he so much as hiccupped. As we unhooked him and prepared to take him home, I looked in panic at our nurse and said, "Ginny, I've just been watching the monitors to make sure he's OK. What am I supposed to do now, just make sure he looks pink and warm?" To which she answered nonchalantly, "Yep, works pretty well."

EL: Get over the sleep deprivation – deal with it. But try to have someone watch the baby, so you can nap sometime during the day. Even an hour will rejuvenate you.

EM: Try to make your needs and expectations clear to family and friends for when the baby arrives – tell them how they can help you. Also, don't let visitors hold your sleeping baby for hours while you entertain them. You should be sleeping during that time – those moments are too rare to gift to someone else for long periods of time.

HA: Until you told us, we didn't know that we had to clean our baby so thoroughly, e.g., between all the folds in her armpit, etc.

Also, watch Dr. Harp's video as soon as possible.

HM: It gets easier. Well, it changes. The same thing won't be hard forever. So don't think about the next stage – just be where you are, cleaning those poops. Because that slows down when you start doing the solid food – it all comes in stages. You won't have to do it all at one time. It feels overwhelming, but try to just be present. People will say, "It goes fast," but that sounds crazy to you. And let me tell you, it doesn't – not until they are much older. So don't even try to rush. Just sit and take deep breaths, and don't borrow worries you don't yet have. They'll come when these leave – and you'll be ready for them then.

Get your baby or babies on a sleep schedule. We didn't do this with our eldest, but we did it with the twins. What a HUGE difference. They sleep better and put themselves to sleep. There's a reliable routine. It's a HUGE relief. Babies will sleep – it's tough, but if you do it early enough, they cry a LOT less than when they are older. Unless they have something wrong that hurts, they don't cry very long and fall asleep. An unpredictable schedule is insanity inducing.

JB: Stay away from the internet if you are panicking. Call/email someone you can trust.

Find someone you trust who you can ask questions. You'll have more questions than you even can begin to think of.

JD: It's good to get together with other new moms, so you can meet others who are struggling just like you are. No one else will care as much as you do about poopy diapers.

JG: Relax and keep your baby skin-to-skin.

Just start talking with mothers about their birthing experiences. Most mothers are happy to share. Besides if you have any challenges, you might have talked with someone who went through the same thing, and you will know exactly who to call for sympathy or advice.

JM: Make lists before the baby comes for things you'll need – grocery shopping, pets' grooming appointments, vacuuming the house... People will want to help you, so have a clear idea of what you'd like them to do.

JR: It is going to be fine, and you are probably not the first mom to do X and be mortified or concerned. Embrace flexibility. Search out other moms as sounding boards and take offers to help with chores or food, if they are offered. You are not superwoman. You can be a supermom. Work out a system with your spouse or partner for care in the first few weeks. Everyone needs their sleep. For the first two weeks, my husband and I had time when we were both up, then I would be in charge of taking care of our daughter until about midnight, then he would take over monitoring crying, soothing, and diapers until about 6:00. He would wake me if I needed to feed her, but otherwise, it was his show. We were both better rested with this arrangement. I do not nap well during the day, so it was important that I could sleep at night.

JR: Make sure you buy a couple of nursing covers, one to keep in your bag, and one to keep in your car.

KC: Accept help when it's offered. This is something that I often had difficulty with. I've always been very independent, and I hate to feel like a burden, so I wanted to try to do as much myself as possible. In retrospect, though, I wish I would have accepted those offers. My friends and family were offering help out of love, and it would have made life just a little easier. ;)

KF: Know that it may be hard, but with time, most, if not all, problems are resolved.

KG: Don't quit trying to breastfeed.

KK2:   I wish I had known it could be difficult – call friends who've breastfed, get support and persevere, but not to the point of sacrificing your mental health.

KP: Have patience with your baby and yourself. Breastfeeding is difficult. Although it's one of the most natural things you could ever do for your child, it takes lots of work and coordination. No one ever learns to ride a bike overnight and the same goes for breastfeeding. There's a reason not everyone does it... it takes patience, coordination, and love. Stick with it and you will soon enough see all of the hard work was worth it.

KS: Don't compare your baby to other babies the same age. Each baby develops in their own time.

KW: Smile and laugh, even in your darkest hour – or at least try. After all, this is supposed to be wonderful and fun, right? Right. And sleep deprivation is like being on good hallucinogenic drugs legally and for free. Bonus!

LG: "It gets better after three months."

LI: Things I wish I'd known before starting breastfeeding...

          1. Breastfeeding, in my opinion, is harder than "natural" childbirth because it lasts so much longer and requires incredible dedication and stamina. I truly believe expectant women should prepare themselves accordingly. We spend so many hours in childbirth prep classes, but we spend very little, if any, time preparing for breastfeeding. Yes, it's something that almost certainly needs to be learned on the job, but some frank discussion about what to expect may ease the shock some women feel that first few weeks and give them the knowledge and strength to carry on. If I had it to do over again, I would've met with a lactation consultant for a personal consultation BEFORE having my son.

          2. Breastfeeding my son has been the hardest thing I have ever done, but also the most fulfilling. The panicked meltdowns that

first week, middle-of-the-night feedings, latch struggles, and ridiculous number of hours spent with my breast pump were all worth it because I can look at him now and know that I did that. I helped "grow" a human being, and for six months after his birth, I was the sole source of his nourishment. That's a profound feeling, and one that can never be taken away from me. It has really opened my eyes to what my body can do, what I can accomplish, and what is important in this life.

3. I felt "icky" for the first many weeks of breastfeeding. My breasts felt weird... sometimes itchy, sometimes tingly, but definitely weird. My breasts also hurt for the first few weeks, and I dare anyone to tell me it doesn't hurt at the beginning. The pain *does go away*, though, once your baby gets the hang of latching on correctly and your breasts have time to get used to the contact.

4. I could not have been successful without my breast pump. My son was in the NICU for his first five days and couldn't nurse, so the pump was the only way I could establish my milk supply during those early days. Once he came home, I nursed and pumped every three hours, supplementing the nursing feedings with expressed milk from a bottle, until we were able to transition to a solid, strong nursing routine.

5. Even when my son started sleeping through the night, I didn't. He started sleeping 10-11 hours per night at three months of age, and that was too long for my breasts to go without emptying. Therefore, I was pumping right before going to bed *and* getting up once in the middle of the night to pump. This wasn't exactly great for my beauty sleep, but I was able to freeze LOTS of extra milk for later!

6. I learned that your nipples don't actually have to be FLAT to be too flat for breastfeeding! My nipples don't look flat to me, but within 30 seconds of walking into our first appointment, Kathy looked at mine and said, "We need to get you a nipple shield!"

7. Nipple shields are a miracle invention. Once I had mine on, my son was able to latch, the sun came out, and the world was a happy place again. Honestly, I had been in such a panic the day before, wondering if I would ever be able to feed my son adequately. The nipple shield helped me do just that for a couple months until

he was strong enough (and my nipples were "out" enough) to go without the shield full time.

8. I wish I knew, while I was bawling my eyes out in a panic that first week, that I would eventually feel like I was actually competent at this. Those first days were SO difficult, but all it took was a little help to nudge me in the right direction and help me take control of the situation.

9. Bonding, for my son and me, was not the immediate, magical moment we all dream of while pregnant, with your little one staring into your eyes lovingly. The first many weeks were a constant struggle just keeping him awake during feedings, and I was so sleep-deprived and anxious about how things were going that I just didn't relax enough to feel it. It DID happen, though... gradually, steadily, and overwhelmingly... and it keeps happening again and again, day after glorious day with him.

LK: - Poop can be virtually any color, don't worry.

- Everything will seem so much easier in a couple months when you get sleep.

- Babies cry – doesn't mean you're a bad mom.

- Gripe water works pretty well for some cranky babies – and it is natural.

- Eventually the baby will be his/her own person and not be so dependent on you.

LT: Make sure you're getting plenty of wet and poopy diapers.

MF: There is no shame in accepting help. Take it, and take it often.

MG: Get outside. Take your babies outside. You need fresh air every day.

MH: Many books tell you how long a feeding "should" last. Read that as a guide. It doesn't mean that you should unlatch the baby when you hit that time or a bit past that time. Use the clock as a guideline. It can help tell you if the baby's feeding routine has changed. The baby will unlatch when he/she is done/has had enough to eat.

If ten seconds go by without the baby sucking, you should stimulate the baby to wake him/her up. One suggestion is rubbing the front of the shoulder (around the clavicle area). Another suggestion is to crawl your fingers up the baby's back along his/her spine. If the baby comes on and off the breast or comes off the breast a lot sooner than normal, he/she may have a bit of gas. Try burping the baby, and then continue the feeding.

MK: If you are having a problem and need help, ask for it immediately. In my experience, so many breastfeeding problems spiral out of control quickly, so addressing them immediately is important.

MM: Nipple cream is great and helped me in the beginning with pain and soreness and dryness when I started breastfeeding.

I wish someone told me about cluster feeding in the beginning. I thought I was doing something wrong because I couldn't understand why my baby always wanted to eat – especially when he went through his growth spurt the second week.

OO: Be patient.

PB: Just take things day by day and do not worry about what may or may not happen tomorrow.

RA: If you have a c-section, ask for the hospital's lactation consultant to visit you in your room for about an hour on your FIRST DAY. She can evaluate your latch, show you hunger cues from your baby, and tell you how to know when baby is done eating. Ask them to fit you for a hospital-grade pump and have them WATCH you set it up and pump to be sure you are doing that correctly (again, to avoid hurting yourself and delaying your success in the early weeks).

Also, be sure to be "asleep" at some point in the first day when the nurses come in, so they can teach your husband how to change the diaper!

RB: - ASK ASK ASK (and ask again) if your baby might need his/her frenulum snipped! We saw three lactation consultants and three pediatricians that first week, but it wasn't until Kathy McCue suggested we have a consult that my daughter's frenulum problem was fixed. I so much wish I'd have asked about that earlier, since she wasn't able to have that corrected until she was about a month old.

- I wish I'd known that pumping isn't easy for everyone at first. For me, it was hard to figure out how and when to get it done, when you are still in those very messy first weeks and months. Tips and tricks for fitting pumping into your day would be helpful for new moms.

- Kathy also suggested that we use a white noise machine, and we found that two small machines that make ocean sounds were so very helpful to us. They seriously helped us stay sane – and more importantly helped soothe my daughter. She would cry and cry, but as soon as we held her near the ocean sounds, she would relax and fall asleep. It was amazing, and I had no clue how helpful that could be. We still use a sound machine that makes ocean, rain, and lullaby sounds during naptime and nighttime.

RO: For me it was important to let my husband be involved in all aspects of baby care, even if I felt that I could do a better/faster/cleaner job. I'm a type A, do it myself type of person, and I knew going in that it would be a challenge to let go of control, but I'm so glad I did. It makes him feel more involved, and it means that I have someone who truly co-parents instead of just doing whatever I ask him to do. I think it also contributes to the bond that he has with our daughter.

SH: I wish I would have read up more on breastfeeding before birth.

SI: Take it one day at a time. When you least expect it that adorable needy blob of a baby, who has had no regard for your exhaustion or feelings or need for a shower, will smile at you (not a gassy smile, but a real smile), and it will make all of the exhaustion and bleeding nipples worthwhile.

SK1:   Keep trying! I loved Jack Newman's nipple cream and "soothies." Try not to read too much and self diagnose online... it can make you crazy!

SK2:   Be prepared that as with anything, experts may give conflicting advice. Pick what seems best for you and your family.

SP: Accept help when it's offered, and even ask for it. Don't beat yourself up for not being able to "do it all." Find mom friends.

SS: Seek out a lactation consultant. Before I had my daughter, I did not even know such a thing existed! It was such a help to my family! Also, there is a great program called SMILE for African American women in Montgomery County, MD, that provides you with an excellent breast pump if you cannot afford to buy or rent one.

TT1: Accept help.

TT2: Do what works for you. You can breastfeed exclusively. You can combine breastfeeding with pumping. That means you can breastfeed once a day and pump the rest of the day, vice versa, or something in between. You can pump exclusively. And if it's really that bad for you, you can give your kid formula and she'll still be okay.

UG: Do what works best for your household, even if it doesn't follow established norms.

WC: Don't be afraid to put your foot down about visitors. It's okay to tell people that you need rest, and they can visit the baby later on.

Kathy's Thoughts:

This is an interesting and thoughtful chapter. I appreciate the intense honesty of how these moms' shared their experiences.

Visitors should be kept to a minimum in the early days, so you can learn how to become a family together.

The nipple cream mentioned is Dr. Jack Newman's APNO (All Purpose Nipple Ointment).

Growth spurts do cause very frequent nursings. Very often, moms feel there's something wrong with their supply when babies want to feed so frequently. When newborns are gaining one ounce per day, then there's nothing to worry about. Remember, babies don't wear watches; they only know how their tummies feel.

Getting past the first month or so is critical to breastfeeding success. Tenacity is important.

Moms temporarily become right-brain dominant after giving birth, so writing things down can be very helpful and important.

Getting out for a walk or running an errand can be a saving grace for many moms. It's my belief that babies enjoy it, too!

Many moms find it difficult to let go and "allow" others to help. It can feel like a sign of weakness to them. We put a lot of pressure on ourselves to prove we are good mothers and don't want to fail.

I remember when my babies were born I had no help at home and no local family. I must have looked like "death warmed over" shuffling out to my mailbox one morning because my neighbors sent their nanny over who just knocked on my door and said, "I'm here to help." In retrospect, I should have thrown my arms around her and dragged her into the house. My psyche and ego, however, would have none of it... I sent her back home. I now have great compassion for and understanding of my situation at that time. I think that experience makes me a better practitioner and perhaps that's why I can empathize so well with my moms. If you've lived with an experience, you can understand it in others.

The painful story shared about the abusive nanny reminds me of the day I came home from work and found my two- and three-year-olds playing in a blow-up pool, with my nanny sound asleep in the chair next to them. I was horrified and paralyzed. Like the mom telling us her story, I, too, did not fire her on the spot. How does one prepare for a situation like this?

Perhaps you, the reader, think it unbelievable that neither of us could bring ourselves to fire our nannies on the spot, but many of the decisions we make as new mothers are difficult. Preparing you and giving rise to new insight is the reason behind this book.

Biggest Hurdle to Overcome

Question 4. What were your biggest hurdles to overcome and how did you overcome them?

The women responded both about hurdles to do with breastfeeding and hurdles that they went through generally in having a newborn.

Hurdles with Breastfeeding...

AB: The heavy burden I placed on myself to do everything possible to breastfeed or give my child breastmilk. I haven't overcome this yet.

AC: My baby came up with jaundice – luckily my milk came in early, so I was able to pump and nurse him. We were released from the hospital, but had three days in a row of blood work, and each time his levels were borderline. I pumped and nursed around the clock, and it worked – we kept him out of the hospital! Such a relief to be able to give baby what he needed.

BN: Not making enough milk. I did not want my daughter to be formula-fed, I wanted to breastfeed until she was a year. Due to reflux and a slow letdown, my daughter would not eat enough. I overcame this a couple of ways. I worked with Kathy, who reassured me that there was nothing wrong with me and nothing wrong with needing to supplement with formula. I decided that any breastmilk was good for my daughter and that I would provide her breastmilk for as long as I could, even if that means that 95% of her milk was formula, at least 5% was breastmilk. I also decided that my next child will love my breasts so much, they will want to breastfeed until junior high school.

BW: I had to overcome nipple pain during breastfeeding. Alternating between breastfeeding and pumping REALLY helped.

CB: Nipple soreness – it took time to stick it out and multiple visits to the lactation consultant for me to get a comfortable position and latch. Again, nipple sandwich... make sure the whole nipple and areola is soft and squishy before baby latches on.

CK: My biggest challenge is low milk supply, and I'm still working on making sure it's where it should be. I was determined from the very beginning to breastfeed my baby exclusively for at least a year. That determination helped me weather a lot of storms. Right now, I'm taking domperidone, and I wish I had started taking it earlier. But you live and learn!

DA: My daughter had problems latching and also gaining weight. I used a contact nipple shield, which helped her latch, but ultimately I became primarily a pumper. It's not so terrible. Give your pump a name – mine was Ethel for a while – it'll make you feel better about the very intimate relationship you're having!

EL: With breastfeeding, I finally found a consultant (albeit later than I should have - I struggled for the first month) that made it work. Domperidone, miracle nipple cream, and a hospital grade pump did wonders for me. Healed my nipples, increased my milk supply, and gave me flexibility with the rigorous feeding schedule. Without that, I might have given up, unable to sustain breastfeeding.

EM: Breastfeeding – I found good help. Also my family thought that I'd be traveling to visit them with the baby, and that they would see the baby whenever they wanted and babysit the baby immediately. I am still overcoming this issue, but I just try to communicate to them that they should probably try to enjoy the baby without needing to babysit. Also, when my family sees me breastfeeding, they act like they just accidentally walked in on me in the bathroom. We are still working on that one.

HA: Milk production and knowing I was doing ok at it. I feel that having the correct pump and getting good sleep/ rest has the best impact for me. I used to sleep on the sofa to allow my husband to sleep, but once I switched back to my bed and brought my baby with me, it was a big help.

JB: With breastfeeding – pumping at work. Helped by re-arranging my pumping times and finding ways to get work done, even when I was pumping.

Increasing my volume when my baby began to want more – same as above.

JD: Low milk supply. I did the best that I could to put forth an effort that I am comfortable with. I have made peace with the fact that my choices might seem odd to others, but they have resulted in a good compromise for me.

JR: Nursing in public.

JR: Making sure that my daughter had enough milk. We worried about low birth weight, but kept at it, and just kept nursing. She is not big, but she is healthy. It is fine to resist the urge to switch to formula, but you need to be in touch with a lactation specialist or your pediatrician along the way to ensure that your baby who might not be gaining oodles of weight is still healthy. The first two to three weeks of breastfeeding are the most trying. It gets easier every day, and definitely after the first two to three weeks.

KC: Lack of sleep. In as much as my husband wanted to help, breastfeeding (or even pumping…) means it largely falls on the mom to be up every few hours. It's exhausting – and that doesn't help your ability to cope. Try to nap when you can. I pumped enough milk to make an extra bottle, so that my husband could take one feeding.

KF: The pain associated with breastfeeding was really shocking. All the books said it would disappear within two to three weeks, but it lasted for more like six to seven weeks for me. I used lanolin, slept without a bra, and worked to always get a deep latch, but really, I just had to ride it out. I still have sharp pains in my breasts when my milk glands are filling. At first, I worried about not having enough milk (I had enough, just had a voracious growing baby) and then I worried I had too much milk (baby was choking on the force of the milk).

KG: Mastitis, overproduction, and spraying my son, unless I pumped some off first. No one I talked with at my doctor's office said this could be an issue. And, colic that was due to dairy in my diet. I underwent many weeks of non-bonding because my son cried so much until I went off dairy – then he became a different, happy child.

KK2: I had huge obstacles and overcame what I could; diabetic, c-section and child in the NICU= stress and flat nipples, all of which precluded normal production. I pumped, got lactation assistance, called friends, ate the right foods, took a galactogogue, tried everything, also used a nipple shield. Never fully overcame, as my production maxed out at 2½ ounces in one full day of eight pumpings (½ hour each).

KP: Breastfeeding was and has been my biggest obstacle. Constantly being so hard on myself and questioning my abilities. Wondering if I was making enough and if I was nursing enough. Am I nursing long enough? In the end, you need to listen to and watch your baby's cues. He will let you know if he's not getting enough. He will tell you if he is still hungry. Be sure to not watch the clock, but watch him and his needs. You figure out the rest.

KW: Breastfeeding has been my biggest hurdle. I didn't realize how difficult it would be for me.

I sought the help of a good lactation consultant, who got me straightened out after I'd already started off on the wrong foot. I hobbled into her office, looking and feeling like I'd been run over by a truck, and in pain. She gave me some "no nonsense" information, helpful nursing supplies, a good pump, and the confidence I needed to make it work. And work it did, with effort and teamwork over time.

I have flat nipples and I didn't know it. In my opinion, my nipples stood up and paid attention at all the right times, so I didn't consider them to be "flat," and, therefore, had skipped right over those sections in the breastfeeding literature I'd read prior to giving birth. I spent the first few days after the baby was born trying to get him to latch the way I understood he should latch from books, the diagram on the hospital room wall, and a brief visit from the hospital's lactation consultant on the day I was leaving the hospital. What I didn't understand was that due to my flat nipples, my baby wasn't able to get a standard correct latch without causing me a great deal of pain. And after days of trying to force him to latch that way, he wasn't getting enough to eat, my nipples were beat up and bleeding, and I was frustrated to tears.

When I finally did get some solid advice from Kathy, I was able to gradually heal my nipples, find a latch that worked for my baby, and over time, get to a point where I am nursing exclusively versus mostly pumping and bottle-feeding (now with only one bottle of expressed breastmilk at bedtime). I've been able to overcome all of this without supplementing with formula (except for the two bottles of formula we gave him in the hospital when we had a weight loss scare) or jeopardizing my baby's nourishment.

Breastfeeding was part sheer stubbornness (I was bound and determined to do what I thought was best for my kid, which was breastfeeding), part support from family and new friends and lactation consultants, and part the grace of God that I stuck with it and that it did get better after the first ten weeks.

MK: I have had mastitis four times (and have only been breastfeeding for six months)! Mastitis is miserable, and I don't wish it on my worst enemy. Thankfully, it is treatable with antibiotics. What gets me through it each time is knowing how much I am doing for my daughter by breastfeeding her. That, and knowing how much I enjoy this special relationship with her!

MH: My biggest hurdle was accepting the fact that no matter how many books I read or re-read and how hard I tried on my own, my baby and I needed help mastering the latch and learning how to easily and correctly unlatch when we got it wrong. After weeks of bleeding and dreading feedings (even though my baby was gaining enough weight), I finally got the help of two lactation consultants. The first one's help didn't really click. It wasn't until I found a lactation consultant that made sense to me that I was able to start feeling like I was successfully feeding my baby.

MM: Not being able to produce enough milk in the beginning. I read information regarding breastfeeding, rented a hospital-grade pump, and talked with an experienced lactation consultant, who was also a nurse practitioner (Kathy McCue!!). It was great to have someone show me tips you couldn't pick up in a book.

RA: Nipples bled, scabbed over, baby lost >10% weight, so we were REQUIRED to put her on formula while in the hospital. Had I not had a c-section, we'd have been released from the hospital before she was that light, and thus no one would have "worried" because she was acting just fine. No lethargy or signs of "starvation," so at home I'd have just kept breastfeeding and by the two-week appointment, I'm sure she'd have been fine... I resent that the hospital put her on formula supplement because that made it easy for me to say just feed her formula while I keep resting. My resting from the pump meant not promoting breastmilk to be made and delayed my getting her enough milk – thus the vicious cycle began and lasted for about three weeks.

My biggest hurdle was thinking I was not making enough milk (she didn't gain rapidly), so I used formula. The day I stopped formula entirely (at three weeks) was when I found I COULD make milk. She has been breastfeeding exclusively for five weeks now and gained on target over the last month (i.e., one ounce per day).

I got over hurdles because of a VERY compassionate lactation consultant named Kathy McCue, who is the ONLY reason I succeeded. She kept telling me I was "normal" to have these experiences and that it wasn't a lost cause (when I was seconds away from giving up breastfeeding, she said I could do it and increase my milk supply, even after three weeks of difficulty). She was right and no formula needs since. Baby is MUCH happier, less gassy, less fussy, since being breastfed exclusively. Our lives are much better. She even sleeps at night!!!

Communication is how I got over my issues. I texted other recent moms I knew, and they told me it would get better. They said I should eat more and drink more. They said they had issues, and now it is fine, only breastfeed, so I could, too. I didn't believe they could have had it as hard as I did, but when Kathy said I was "normal," I just relaxed and succeeded!!! THANKS A MILLION!!!

RB: Breastfeeding was so hard for me at first, but I asked for help, advice, reassurance, and support from many people - friends,

SE: With my first child, I was never really happy breastfeeding. It caused me more anxiety than joy. I probably should have stopped sooner than I did, so I could enjoy her more, but I felt "guilty." Don't ever feel guilty about making a decision that is best for you as a mom.

SH: Poor latch in the first day or so and low milk supply.

Lots of consultations with lactation experts.

SI: Making enough milk (which continues to be a struggle). My lactation consultant and her support, the support of my family, and Kellymom.com helped me get to a point where I am a little less obsessive about the amount of milk I make and am able to provide my daughter. I know that I am doing everything, so that helps.

SK1: My nipples were soft and short. They had a lot of toughening up to do!!! Our baby would latch on like a barracuda and chomp and pull. Kathy taught me different positions and taught me how to use a pump to give my nipples a break. Once my milk supply became more established and my nipples toughened up and became thicker, it became easier. Now they can handle the barracuda!!

SK2: Getting baby's weight back up with feedings every two hours. Mommy was not willing to sacrifice her or baby's sleep to do this, so it fell on daddy. Pediatrician's office and lactation consultant had us schedule many visits to ensure baby was gaining adequately.

SP: With nursing our singleton, the biggest hurdle was the latch. I was able to get Lucy to eventually open wide and nurse well, but each session started with chomping that made me see stars. Also, the nurses at the hospital advised me to not nurse more frequently than every three hours. Which was TERRIBLE advice! With the twins, one of them had low muscle tone, and it was difficult to get her to latch and suck hard enough and stay latched. We bungled through the first month or two, with me nursing them individually. Once latch had been perfected with both of them, I was able to switch to nursing them simultaneously, which helped a lot with letting down the milk. The stronger nurser (Kate) enabled both sides to flow. It makes me grateful that the one with low muscle tone (Frances) is a twin! She certainly got to benefit from more milk and a longer duration of nursing than if she'd been a singleton.

Our first child is now seven, and I breastfed her for 13 months. It was an incredibly rocky start, but once we got the hang of it, and once my mangled nipples healed, we were pros. When she was three years old, our twin girls arrived. I nursed them for 15 months. That was less of a rocky start, but much more of a complete and utter full-time job! And I felt like a circus act when they were older, nursing simultaneously, and trying to punch each other while they slurped. :)

SS: The quantity in which you must pump! The only way I overcame this is the desire NOT to want to give my daughter formula!

TT2: With my first daughter, the biggest hurdle was the pain. She was tongue-tied and it felt like she had spikes in her gums that were gnawing on my nipples. When I got home from the hospital, I told my husband that I couldn't do it anymore and to please go get the formula. He came back to me with the breast pump and said, "Try this first." So I did. And it was much less painful than the breastfeeding. I pumped exclusively for three months, until I went back to work.

With my second daughter, the biggest hurdle is going to be continuing to breastfeed/pump after I go back to work. I'm a senior manager for the federal government. It's hard to get away from work. It's also hard to take your clothes off at work. Thank goodness for the hands-free bra. It will allow me to continue working while I pump.

Hurdles With Caring for a Newborn

AA: My baby always wanted to be held, and I had to teach her to be independent.

AT: Our baby would not sleep anywhere other than our chest until ten weeks.

80

BR: I remember feeling completely overwhelmed with having twins and feeling completely incompetent with them. However, over time, you just get used to each other and things get better.

CV: So much of what you go through when you have your first baby is overcome by the passage of time. New moms should cling to that. In the middle of those first four to eight weeks, you really can think your life is over, your nipples are going to fall off, you're never going to feel like yourself again, you're never going to have sex again... and I definitely was not prepared for the emotional and mental turmoil that ensued. My biggest hurdles with my first were that I had a 30-hour labor that ended with a fourth degree tear after my daughter came out like a bowling ball on the third suction attempt and that she was jaundiced and terrible at nursing. I spent six straight weeks on a feeding cycle that gave me 30-60 minutes in between feedings and pumpings, 24/7. I - WAS - EXHAUSTED.

With my second, everything was so much easier. My labor and delivery was less than two hours from start to finish, my son came out entirely naturally, healing was easy, and nursing was much easier. He did get jaundiced, too, and I had to pump a lot, but because I had been through it before, I knew everything was going to be okay. The moral is take solace in the knowledge that others have done it before you and survived. And get help if you think you might be depressed.

DG: Our baby has acid reflux. At about three weeks old, she just screamed and screamed. Feedings were taking forever, and she just cried and writhed (as if in pain), and I had no idea what was going on. She threw up a lot, and I just assumed I was doing something wrong. When I explained the problems to the pediatrician, they didn't say anything about GERD. So I just suffered through it and cried and cried. It was hard. Had I known what symptoms to look for and to ask the pediatrician about (explicitly), I think we would have saved my sanity and a lot of tears. Once diagnosed (and medicated), she was a whole new baby. It was like magic.

DK: My baby would not sleep during the day. He cried *a lot* and it never occurred to me that it was because he was tired. I assumed if he was tired, he would sleep, and it must be hunger/gas/reflux or some other malady. In reality, he was exhausted, and once I learned when he needed to sleep and what needed to happen to make sure he did, it made a huge difference.

DS: Postpartum mood swings were my biggest difficulties. I don't think I actually had postpartum depression, but I definitely had significant emotional instability for at least a month after my son was born, and I think my husband's steadiness and time were the key factors in overcoming that. My husband actually called a friend, who had two children at the time, to ask him what was going on and how he should handle it. He got a reassuring, although not necessarily helpful, "Yeah, that's pretty normal, you kinda gotta just ride it out and encourage her when you can."

I think I cried multiple times a day for the first week, and at least once a day for a couple weeks after that. Sometimes it was over things that felt worth crying about (my son being stuck in the Special Care Nursery on all kinds of machines and medications), sometimes it was about things that I knew were ridiculous and insignificant, but I couldn't help it, and sometimes I had no idea what I was crying about. At times, it made it hard to pick up my son to try to nurse him or think about doing anything else, but fortunately each of those swings was pretty short. In time, as my hormones settled down and I realized that my baby was thriving and I was healing, I even made it back to a pretty normal emotional state.

EL: Pain (hemorrhoids) and sleep deprivation. With the hemorrhoids, I finally found Bottom Balm (Earth Mama Angel Baby) and Lidocaine.

EM: My family thought that I'd be traveling to visit them with the baby, they would see the baby whenever they wanted, and babysit the baby immediately. I am still overcoming this issue, but I just try to communicate to them that they should probably try to enjoy the baby without needing to babysit.

HM: For me the hurdles were, and still are, feeling trapped, isolated, and lonely. Also, the stress can build up and become a barricade to treating yourself and others well. Schedule time to be with other people. Exercise. I know it's hard when you feel like crap and just want to sit and watch TV and drink wine. But let me tell you, burning off that stress and getting a good dose of companionship will help you a million times more. And it helps you sleep and feel more rested when you do rest.

JG: After my son was born, he was in the NICU for 105 days, and I was working full time an hour away. The hardest thing was to find energy to do everything that needed to be done. I followed the advice from a friend and took it day by day, and sometimes just ten minutes at a time. I also reminded myself that this was all temporary, things would be better, even though it did not really seem like that everyday. There were a lot of days that I did just take it ten minutes at a time and ended up surviving the entire day.

JM: Fatigue. Fifteen months out, I'm still trying to overcome this one.

JR: Sleep deprivation wears off around week three and you feel energetic by week six.

KK1: Dealing with my baby's feeding/digestive issues has been tough (reflux, milk protein allergy, chronic constipation, tongue-tie), but I've just tried to make sure I address all my concerns with doctors and specialists, and do my own research, so I can understand what is going on. I also had a hard time coming to terms with being sticky, wet, and messy all the time from all the drool/excrement/spit-up/snot – I guess I've just become desensitized to it now!

KP: One of the most devastating things I did to myself was compare with a friend. A friend of mine had her second child a week before mine. Although this was a great opportunity to support one another, I often turned it into a chance to compare my parenting abilities to hers. After all, this was her second child, and she was much more experienced. From comparing weights to nursing session lengths to lengths of sleeping stretches, I always doubted what I was doing if it did not align to her and her baby. I drove myself crazy. You will have many chances in life to doubt your parenting abilities... try not to start the habit so early on!

KS: Friends giving me advice on what I should do with the baby, classes to register them for, how I should feed them, dress them, etc. Listen to your gut, you are the best expert for your baby.

LG: Time and patience.

LK: Postpartum depression... took meds that I learned were compatible with breastfeeding.

Sleep... realized I couldn't function unless I let someone else feed her sometimes, so I could sleep.

LT: Adjusting to not having as much time for myself (whether it's exercising, working, seeing friends) or for my husband. I have found that I'm a better mother if I take time to do these things, and thankfully I have a supportive husband, who also realizes this, and gives me the time to do things for myself (as I do for him).

MF: Getting into a routine with a newborn is the hardest thing I have ever had to do. I was exhausted, delirious, trying to recover from a c-section, and still trying to keep everyone (husband, my son, my family, etc.) happy, and keep up with my pre-baby routine. It's just not going to happen. You have to learn to let the laundry pile up and let crap lay everywhere because it's more important to heal from childbirth and bond with your baby. All the other stuff can wait.

MG: Surrendering control over my schedule. I'm still getting used to that, but breathing through it helps! Operating on less sleep (so now I learn to go to bed earlier).

MH: The biggest hurdle was accepting that this is one area of life where there is no real instruction manual. You can read all the books you want to get insight and opinions. At the end of the day, you need to figure out what is right for you and your baby. Six months in, I still struggle with this concept.

OO: Teaching my son to sleep through the night.

PB: Not getting frustrated or worrying about outcomes or how it may be the next day – I haven't quite figured it out yet!

RO: Sleep deprivation was really hard on me for the first few months. I napped a lot, but there was nothing to be done other than live through it. One of our neighbors gave us some good advice when we were worrying about our daughter crying during her baths. He said that we should just consider everything a phase that will pass, and that has proved to be a very effective way to get through hard moments.

SI: Learning that the baby would be safe when she slept. Our first night at the hospital, just as I was falling asleep, she vomited amniotic fluid. This sent me into a panic and made me fearful of not supervising her sleep. To the point that I would stay up to watch her sleep, consequently I would not sleep for days. It took me a long time, and many discussions with family and doctors, to understand that she would not die if she spit up at night.

TT1: Postpartum hormones were very rough – it was such a dark time. I was soooo happy to have my baby, but it was very dark, with feelings of hopelessness – talk about it, realize that it's normal and ok.

UG: I had to let go of thinking I could control my day and had to be more flexible. I think patience starts to come more easily when you have a child, simply because you have no choice. And meditating didn't hurt, which is something I do a few times a day.

WC: Adjusting to a different pace of life.

Kathy's Thoughts:

Although I'm very grateful for all the nice compliments I received from some of these moms, all I did was to hold up a mirror. Every mom has it in her to succeed, it's just confidence that is sometimes lacking. Confidence in knowing we can be the mother we've always wanted to be. I just offer encouragement and occasional direction.

It's like being lost on a road and meeting someone that tells you you're on the right path and headed in the right direction. You can just keep moving forward to reach your destination.

Most Unexpected Part of Becoming a New Mother

Question 5. What was the most unexpected part of becoming a new mother?

We are all inundated with information on raising children. We get information from our doctors, our parents, we see media representations of parenthood, and we see friends and relatives raise their children. There are always, though, the unexpected moments in parenthood that we either heard nothing about or needed to experience it to believe it. For each child, each parent, each time period your baby is born is unique. Some unexpected moments are better than the parents had thought they would be, and some are worse than they thought they would be. I hope that you can learn from these experiences to be prepared or actually be open to be unprepared for the birth of your child. The following are examples of those unexpected things that new parents shared with me.

AA: The huge responsibility of caring for another little human being who cannot express herself.

AB: Not immediately feeling the unconditional love for this 7 lb 5 oz person placed in my arms.

AC: How automatic nurturing baby comes – just letting instincts take over and really succeeding!!

AT: Living in the dichotomy. Everything feels so small and so big at the same time. Knowing that the big things will feel small in a matter of time, too.

BR: I always felt that I'd have some immediate connection to them and a strong sense that they belonged to me, but when I first saw them, it was like meeting someone new that you've heard about, but you don't really know them. Excited, but nervous whether you'd really get along (if that makes sense). Even now, I have to remind myself that these are my kids. I don't feel that motherhood has changed me as a person much really. I just have more things to keep track of and my memory has gotten really bad. Might be because I had kids at a later age (I was 43), so I had a pretty strong sense of self when I had them. However, having said that, my priorities have completely changed. I make almost all my decisions based on when/whether I get to see them and the degree to which their schedules will be affected (with an eye to keep changes to their schedule at a minimum).

Also, I never thought I'd kiss them as much as I do.

BW: The recovery. And, that my husband still says I'm sexy, even though my body is so different and we can't do it for another couple weeks – lol!

CK: I don't think I realized how "physically demanding" the job of motherhood is. I went to the gym for the first time after delivery when my son turned three months. And I kid you not, I barely broke a sweat doing the same exercise routine I did before his birth. I think taking care of Luke must have been some sort of exercise in itself!

CV: I had no idea how hard it would be to become a mom and feel "trapped," like we couldn't just get up and go anywhere we wanted to anymore.

DG: The amount of time the baby was attached to my breast. And for how long. Twelve months of breastfeeding is a really, really long time. Nine months is a really long time. Six months is a long time. I knew about the time commitment in theory. But in practice, it is really, really hard. Especially for a working mom. And once back at work, taking the time to pump every three to four hours for 15 minutes is a big commitment. I'm scheduled back to back with meetings and travel, so it's nearly impossible to find the time I need to pump. I didn't think about that – very unexpected.

DK: I didn't expect it to be this much fun early on. I thought the fun would come later.

DS: The sheer exhaustion. I did not realize how tired someone could be and still function, at least minimally, or how tiredness could be physical, emotional, mental, and spiritual all at once. I also did not realize how drastically sleep deprivation could affect your equilibrium, and even make you feel like you're losing your grip on reality. It's a horrible realization, but some day, probably around 3:00 am, when your baby just is not interested in sleeping, and all you need is some rest, all of a sudden shaken baby syndrome will start to make sense. You will feel like a terrible excuse for a human being, but it's true. Just know that it's normal, that some sleep really will help, and that it's OK to take a break, even if it seems like a bad time. I was in a class with a wise teacher before I became a parent, and I distinctly remember her saying that "the difference between you and an abusive parent is ten seconds where you put the screaming child down and walk away," and I held on to that when I felt like an awful parent for wanting to silence my kid at any cost.

EL: That so much of my day would be about feeding. I thought the tasks would be more equally balanced.

EM: The insanely strong bond that I had with the baby immediately. Some call this "love," but for me, it was very much unlike other loving relationships in my life. When the baby cried, or honestly even sometimes when someone else was holding the baby or walked the baby out of my sight, I would feel physically sick. Something else surprising and wonderful is that even though I'm an impatient person, it's not hard to be patient with the baby. Her dad can't stand the crying, but since my impulse is purely to comfort her, it doesn't get on my nerves like it does with others.

HA: That breastfeeding could take so much effort to get the right milk flow.

HM: I had this idea that I would love it and have this "feeling" of being a mother. I thought I would be different somehow. But I remember the first time I met up with some other mothers to walk with our babies, how odd it felt. I was still me, but I had this person with me. And now I was meeting people just because they had people, too. It felt so weird, and I thought it would feel natural. But that comes with time. And you realize that you ARE the same you – and you won't have some transcendent change that will make you different. The naturalness comes with time. But since things are always changing, you're always a fish out of water. But you get used to that – motherhood forces you to get comfortable with being uncomfortable.

JB: How much of your old activities you put off for the baby and don't miss at all.

JD: I knew lots of babies, but I did not appreciate how overwhelming it is to be the one who's responsible for someone else 24 hours a day.

JG: Having a child born at 26 weeks. Once my child was cleared medically to go home from the NICU, I thought things would get easier. I had more time to spend with my son, but I had no idea that I would be spending so much time with therapists to get him "caught up" with other kids at his age.

JM: Anxiety and frustration, both toward myself and occasionally toward our son. It's not all Kodak moments.

JR: It just felt surreal. We knew we were pregnant and a baby was coming, but then one day you go to the hospital and come home three days later with a baby and your life is forever changed.

JR: Enjoyment of nursing.

KC: The overwhelming sense of love you feel when you see your child for the first time. Every mother expects to love their child – but here is this person you're meeting for the very first time, and yet your heart overflows with love, as though you've known and cared for them your whole life.

KF: How quickly things change! Just when I think that I'm getting the hang of things, new problems/challenges/moods arise.

KG: How great it is – in every way :)

KK1: I don't think anything was really unexpected – I just couldn't imagine it until I was there. For instance, I knew I wouldn't have time to clean up the house and cook dinner like I did before she was born, but I didn't really KNOW until I was in the thick of it.

KK2: The ability to be and feel completely depressed, while knowing that somehow one of the greatest things that can happen in my life had.

KP: At first, I unexpectedly felt a little bitter that I suddenly had to share this little guy with everyone else around me. He and I had started our little bond early on when he would kick at me when my hand was on my belly. He was my little guy, and now I had to share him with everyone around me. I was bitter he couldn't stay "just mine," no matter how badly I was looking forward to meeting him. I found myself a little withdrawn while out on maternity leave in the beginning. Once Daddy went back to work, it was difficult to not have anyone to speak with (that would speak back), and I yearned for conversation that did not revolve around dirty diapers. I found a local Mom's Group that met weekly, and it was a welcome change to meet other new moms, ask questions, and get support from other more experienced moms, and have a reason to leave the house!

KS: How tired I would be and how I would not be able to multi-task as I used to do to get things done. Now my list is shorter. Instead of accomplishing 20 things a day, I accomplish ten and am happy.

KW: Hormones. Hormones. Hormones. They can be sneaky little devils that creep into your brain and skew your perception of reality. They sometimes make you doubt your ability to care for your child. They might make it seem impossible to see the light at the end of the tunnel. They can make you snap at your spouse faster than you can say "chemically imbalanced." Eventually, the unwelcome little buggers will pack up and head out, leaving you stronger and more confident than you thought was possible. Oh, and peaceful and happy – finally.

LG: My sister told me to put the baby in the car seat and walk around the house if she could not stop crying any other way. I remember thinking, "Yeah, right. I am not going to do that. There is no way I will do that." Guess what? I did it. I did it all.

91

LK: - Second child – that I could love a second being as much as I could love my first...

- Expensive!

- Finding out that I was not as patient as I thought I was.

- That I was not instantly bonded to my child, but it did happen eventually.

LT: How attached I would become to Alex. Here I am – totally professional career woman who previously only worried about herself and her husband. Then along comes Alex, and I was absolutely transformed. I always anticipated that I would return to work after giving birth, but when the time came to go back, part of me considered staying home (even though, as my husband says, it would drive him and me crazy, because I really do love my job and would miss it!). I just couldn't fathom being away from him all day. I also used to work >12 hour days, staying very late at the office. Now, I'm out of the office everyday by 4:00 pm to get Alex from daycare, and I wouldn't have it any other way.

MH: What you are capable of doing based on your love for your child and your "motherly instincts," no matter how little you feel you inherited them. Your body is challenged in a way it never has been before. I trained and successfully ran a marathon. The dedication and stamina it took to train to run a marathon 1½ years after I got off the couch for the first time lead me to believe I could easily master being a mother. It is more work than I could ever imagine, but I love it. I love my child, and that love and motherly instinct allows me to function on very little sleep. My love for my child and my husband increases every day.

The other unexpected part is that despite the people around you thinking you should instinctively know what to do or have the answers, you don't. That was particularly unexpected as in most areas of my life I have "known the answers."

MF: The enormous boobs!

MG: How long it takes to get them dressed (in snowsuits) and out the door.

MK: That you really never get a break. I had heard all about how much life changes when you become a mom, but it never really hit me that once you are a mom, it's a 24-hour job with no breaks! It's exhausting, but so very amazing.

MM: No, I did not anticipate I would have a c-section, so I was not prepared. I did not anticipate problems breastfeeding. I read magazines, but nothing really prepared me until I was confronted with my problems and had to turn to the nurses at the hospital.

The loss of control I felt over my body and medical conditions (gestational diabetes and pre-eclampsia).

PB: The frequency of feedings and diaper changes.

OO: Dealing with unwanted advice from my own mother.

RA: That baby would sleep well at night. That I would not be able to do anything at all while with baby (as in I seriously thought I'd be able to visit people I've neglected over the last year and could search for a new job while on maternity leave, could organize the house... I'm lucky if I can go to the bathroom sometime within the two hours following the urge to pee!).

Unexpected that I cannot suck in my belly two months post-c-section.

Unexpected to have had so much difficulty breastfeeding. Even less expected was that I COULD breastfeed after three weeks of serious difficulty. Even less expected and seriously appreciated was that the lactation consultant at my pediatrician's office (Kathy) would be my best friend to see me through the most difficult time, so I could succeed at breastfeeding. I never thought I (a normally very strong individual emotionally) would need so much emotional support with breastfeeding. Having Kathy as my cheerleader, who never gave up on me, is the ONLY reason I succeeded. THANK YOU!!!

RB: I expected breastfeeding to be hard, but I didn't think it would be SO hard that it would completely stress me out for many weeks. Honestly, I wondered if I would have any maternal instinct once my baby arrived, but I've found that I'm not quite as clueless as I thought I would be. So my maternal instinct is a nice surprise. :)

RO: I was surprised by new feelings for my husband. I guess I didn't expect that much to change, but I think we are bonded in a whole new way now.

SE: The amount of exhaustion. I had never been so tired. Pulling all nighters in college to finish a paper is no comparison to the amount of sleep deprivation most new parents go through.

SI: The love that I feel for my daughter, at times it is overwhelming.

SK1: How hard breastfeeding was!

SK2: Postpartum hormones really can seem to run the show, even if you didn't feel pregnancy ones.

SP: I think what I least expected was how subsumed my identity would be, for so long. It's only recently (the kids are now seven, four, and four years old) that I feel like I'm beginning to remember who I am apart from being a mother.

SS: How you must seek accommodations in the workplace in order to pump at work.

TT1: How much I LOVE my baby and how instant it was, it was so much more intense than I thought.

TT2: I expected to be able to breastfeed without a problem. I'm smart, hard working, courageous – and I knew the benefits of breastfeeding my child. I figured I'd have no problem. I was wrong. I had a huge problem. But I did the best I could and that's all one can ask for.

UG: The hours – its 24 hours, seven days a week. No one or no book can fully prepare you for that.

Kathy's Thoughts:

So, what can all these unexpected experiences teach you? It teaches you to RELAX and be open to the unexpected joys and pitfalls of your unique experience of parenthood. Enjoy the ride!

It's also helpful to remember that moms become right brain dominant in the early months after delivering. That phenomenon occurs so moms can better sync with their babies... goo goo ga ga kind of communication; lots of smiling, snuggling, and kissing, too! The thinking, logic side is temporarily gone. So, give yourself a break if you cannot do the things you expected to be able to do.

Best Part of Becoming a Mother

Question 6. What was the best part of becoming a mother?

As you will see throughout this book, I usually read all the responses, and then see if they fit into categories based on some common theme. In a way, I did that here – but there is only one common theme: the baby!

Some of the comments in subsequent chapters may, at times, sound like little horror stories. As you read them, keep in mind that despite their travails, not one of those writers would ever want to go back to a life without their baby. It's a love like you've never known before and is unlike any other relationship you will ever have. So when the going gets rough, remember to keep your eyes on the prize … *your* baby.

AA: The joy my baby brings into my life is something which I cannot express in words.

AB: Learning to love this 7 lb 5 oz person placed in my arms. Working with my husband, together, to get through each day.

AT: Being in love with my child.

BN: Hugging, kissing, tickling, playing, singing, reading, and being with my daughter. I had no idea that I could love like this. I love her more than I have any words to express. It may be cliche, but this love is unlike any other.

BR: Getting hugs and kisses from my kids.

BW: Seeing my baby grow from week-to-week and feeling even closer to my hubby.

CB: A new range of emotions you never knew you had. I always felt bad when I watched bad stories about kids on the evening news, but now I full out cry. The connection to your kids is stronger than anything else!

CK: My baby, my baby, my baby. :-)

CV: The best part was watching the life my husband and I created out of love grow and change and burp and cry and poop (projectile onto our clothes once).

DG: I have the most beautiful baby ever. I love her smiles, her squeals, and her cuddles. She makes my heart melt. When I get home from work, I get her in my arms and everything else disappears.

DK: I just love the little guy so much.

DS: I was out shopping recently and saw a picture frame that said "Grandchildren fill a hole in your heart you never knew was there." I can't speak for grandparenthood, but it explained everything I've felt about motherhood. I never felt like anything was missing from my life before Avery came along, but by the end of his first week, I couldn't remember life without him or figure out how on earth I had been happy before him. Here was this tiny gift that had been given to me, that took my already wonderful life and added delight, wonder, and joy on a daily basis. As much as the sleep deprivation and self-doubt made the first ten weeks agonizingly difficult, the tiny weight of my son sleeping on my bare chest made me feel like this is what I was made for.

EL: The smiles. I still can't believe them when I see them – absolutely overwhelming.

EM: The baby is actually FUN! Also the new sense of purpose is wonderful. My previous stresses seem insignificant.

HA: Everyday I am so happy to see my little girl and to spend time with her. Our whole family dynamic has changed.

HM: Snuggles. Babies can't communicate for a long time, and it can be hard. You want to know what they need, what they want. You find yourself overwhelmed with trying to figure that out all the time. But they do communicate in snuggles. They need you and want you, like air and water. So just soak up those snuggles. They are saying thank you, I love you, and telling you everything is okay and will be okay.

And later – reading. Reading books together is about the best thing in the world. They tell you little things and comments and ask questions – so much goes on in those moments.

JB: Getting to know your little one and watching her grow. Every day is something new.

JD: My daughter looks at me as if she's fascinated, and it's exciting knowing how important I am in her world. I could stare at her for hours.

JG: My son has stolen a little piece of my heart. I love seeing him interact with the world.

JM: Our son is awesome and continues to impress me. Motherhood taps into a well of emotion – mostly positive – that I didn't know was there.

JR: Taking care of a dynamic wee one and getting to play with her.

JR: The overwhelming amount of love you have for your child.

KC: Watching my son grow and develop before my eyes. He's almost ten months now, and it's such an exciting time because, on an almost weekly basis, he can do something new that he wasn't able to do the previous week.

KF: Nurturing a sweet little baby. Evolution is one sneaky mother: I'm in love with the little guy.

KG: The best part is that you get nurtured back. That's been a wonderful surprise for me.

KK1: Just having my daughter as part of our life! She's so much fun!

KK2: The miracle that this little human had gestated inside of me for 9-9 ½ months and that he was mine, all mine.

KP: I always wanted to be a mother. Always. But no one prepares you for the love you feel for this little one when he smiles back at you for the first time. No one prepares you for the amazing bond you develop through breastfeeding and the feeling of joy you have that this little one is solely dependent upon you.

KS: Holding the baby, feeding the baby late at night, and that bonding time, and now the baby smiling and talking (squealing) when you see them. Watching the baby develop and remembering by writing down all the milestones each week.

KW: Just watching the miracle of development in your baby from day to day. It is just amazing how quickly they grow, change, and learn. And how readily they come to show their happiness and love for their parent(s). I've particularly enjoyed how it has given me an excuse to SLOW DOWN and soak up every minute.

LG: As the months pass by, my little baby falls in love with me more and more. She smiles real big when I come in the room, and it is still getting better and better. She is only nine months now and so much fun.

LK: Smiles, laughter, and snuggle time with my kids.

LT: Watching my son grow up and do all sorts of new things (crawling, walking, etc.).

MF: Holding my baby in my arms and staring at her for hours on end. When you realize the miracle of life, everything else matters so much less.

MG: Making them smile and laugh. Figuring out their "signals" and how to soothe them.

MH: Watching a little part of my husband and I grow each day and acquire new skills and experiences.

MK: Holding that baby all day long! I would never put her down if I could avoid it! Despite some difficulties, this has been the most amazing experience of my life.

MM: Seeing your baby for the first time and hearing him cry. I immediately fell in love.

OO: Feeling purpose in life.

PB: Being able to look at the baby and be constantly amazed how he/she came about, that he/she is yours, and touching that baby soft skin.

RA: Seeing her smile at me (around five to six weeks). I love snuggling with my newborn.

RB: Wow, that is hard to say. But right now, there is nothing in the world like her smiles and laughs. And watching her grow and learn. And watching my husband play with her.

RO: The baby! Everything about her – her smell, her smiles, the way she rests her head on my shoulder and falls asleep, her fiesty little personality. It's all the best.

SE: Ultimately the sense of empowerment I got from surviving the hard times. You feel like if you can get through this – you can pretty much get through anything. You find strength you never knew you had. As rapidly as your baby grows in the first year, on a personal developmental level, so do you. It's truly amazing.

SH: Experiencing an overwhelming amount of love for my child.

SI: The love that I feel for my daughter and the joy I get from being with her. I went from being a litigating attorney whose career path was set in stone to taking steps to work part time or, hopefully, become a stay-at-home mom. Never saw that coming.

SK1: The physical and emotional connection to your baby.

SK2: Being able to watch a little being grow and to give through breastfeeding; being forced/given a good enough excuse to slow down and be present.

SP: It is an honor to play such a vital role in the lives of these little people and to be privy to their unfolding as individuals.

SS: When my baby smiles!

TT1: Holding my baby.

TT2: I wake each morning eager to see the smile on my daughter's face when I say good morning to her. Her smile lights up the room and she gives the best hugs.

UG: Having a little life that is half of you in your arms.

WC: Experiencing life on a whole different level. Becoming more emotional and sympathetic.

Kathy's Thoughts:

These comments speak for themselves. Here, what is unbelievable is also 100% true. I wholeheartedly agree with everything said.

Worst Part of Experience

Question 7. What was the worst part of your experience?

Perhaps the worst part of any experience is what either can't be foreseen or be dealt with once it happens. The idea that something is "out of control" or "beyond our control" can be pretty scary. In a totally new situation, one that has never been faced before, that out of control feeling can arise quickly. In some cases, we have competence, and we have information, so it should be easy to deal with events. However, if we lack the filter of experience to help us decide on the best option, we can still feel stress and second guess ourselves. Each situation is unique. Even when we do have a gut feel for what we need to do, we also may find that there is so much information to sift through that the burden seems overwhelming. Some of us don't know where to start. And we still have to live with the situation that unfolds.

Here's some thoughts of what moms found so difficult and unexpected that they called it the WORST part of their pregnancy and delivery.

Pregnancy

MM: The morning sickness and medical complications I had to endure during my pregnancy and the physical changes to my body (acanthosis nigricans, linea nigra, moles on my face).

PB: Tough pregnancy.

Birth

BW: The recovery.

CV: The worst part is a tie between having my vagina and rectum become one big gaping hole when my daughter came out, and nursing and pumping so much that I thought my breasts were going to detach and fly across the room.

JG: Having my son pulled from my arms because he had stopped breathing, turned blue, and had to be resuscitated by a group of nurses. This all happened in the NICU under the watchful eye of well-trained medical staff, but it was disturbing none the less.

KK2:   Surgical birth and the entire nightmare that was breastfeeding for me, his NICU stay, and the humility of having had to succumb to the experience that was the antithesis of what I wanted.

MF: Being terrified of the pain once I had given birth before. Recovering from a c-section is the pits, especially when you can't walk up and down stairs and live in a townhouse. Oh, and trying to have sex again after giving birth is excruciating. You feel like a virgin all over again. :)

MG: I had a c-section – the healing process was slower and harder than I expected.

OO: With my second child - labor. Had to argue with my doctor for hours to reduce medical interventions and have a natural birth.

The Baby

DG: The crying associated with the GERD (gastro-esophageal reflux disorder). I read so much that told me that crying was normal. That babies cry for hours for no reason and you just have to deal with it, that it is normal. So I thought her screaming was normal. I didn't realize she was in pain. I had nothing to judge it against, and the crying was just unbearable. It ripped my heart out. I couldn't sleep when she was crying or stay away, it was just really, really hard.

KG: Colic

UG: Feeling completely beholden to my child's schedule.

Breastfeeding

AB: The baby screaming as we tried to nurse for the first few days. The feeling of not knowing how much she was eating.

BB: Breastfeeding.

CB: Breastfeeding (until I finally found my groove after five weeks).

DA: Milk blisters and plugged ducts! They make nursing hurt, but what's worse is that nursing is the best remedy!

EM: Breastfeeding. Also having family be absolutely sure they know better than I do when it comes to the baby. People having input on things that are none of their business, like when to start solids, what I dress the baby in, how long I should breastfeed.

HA: The time during which I was struggling with the milk production and thinking somehow it was my fault, that I wasn't doing something correctly, and that I was failing at it.

HM: With breastfeeding – it was the pain. I had yeast and mastitis, and my nipples hurt so very badly. It was so discouraging. I wanted so badly for it to work out. I wish I'd taken better care of myself and been calmer. I wish I had gotten help and done proper treating and followed instructions better. I wish I hadn't felt like I had to just take it.

KW: Difficulty breastfeeding... combined with hormone overload... combined with sleep deprivation... combined with visiting in-laws... That was my low point.

LK: Thrush.

MK: Aside from my problems with mastitis and milk supply, and in more general terms, I find it difficult and uncomfortable to handle people with well-intended, but ignorant advice with regard to breastfeeding (for example, from people who have never breastfed before)!

RA: Not being prepared for breastfeeding and feeling like I was failing, and not having had serious enough attention to my breastfeeding issues while I was in the hospital and still able to prevent the damage to my nipples, which further delayed breastfeeding success.

Also, I hated the epidural being in for 24 hours after the c-section. I felt trapped and afraid I'd never walk again – but once it was out and my legs were no longer numb, everything was perfectly fine physically, so I'd not hesitate to have an epidural in the future (I just hated it while it was in – again, I'm used to being very independent and that was far too confining). I got it taken out early and was very glad to have requested that.

SI: Lactation consultant at the hospital who informed me, while I was sobbing about how little milk I made, that supplementing was the worst decision I could ever have made for my daughter. The timing of her delivery couldn't have been worse and sent me into a deep funk.

SS: Frequency in which I must pump.

TT1: Having my baby lose 15% of birth weight. The baby was weighed when 36 hours old and had lost some weight, but not enough to be concerned. We were released almost 24 hours later and the baby wasn't weighed again before discharge. She had lost a lot more by the time we got to the pediatrician's office.

Ask the hospital to weigh the baby more than twice during your visit to monitor weight loss.

TT2: When I had trouble breastfeeding, I felt like a failure. And not only did I know I was a failure, but everyone who asked "oh, are you breastfeeding" would know I was a failure, too.

Physical and Emotional Tolls

AA: Sleepless nights and days.

AC: Not knowing about the answer to question 5 (most unexpected part of becoming a new mother) for nine months.

AT: Exhaustion.

BN: The exhaustion. I love sleeping late, I used to sleep until 1:00 on the weekends. I loved laying in bed and watching TV. Now, I struggle to keep my eyes open past 8:00 pm. I can't remember the last time I slept in. The worst part is that the exhaustion has made my husband and I bicker over the most stupid stuff. It is much harder being a new parent when you are fighting with your spouse.

CK: Sleep deprivation. I've sleep-trained my baby, but because he starts sleeping at 7:30 at night, he wakes up at 4:30 in the morning. I wake up with him, so that I can breastfeed him. I'm running on fumes from the accumulated lack of sleep.

DA: Giving into the pressure I felt from my discharge nurse not to take my pain-killers and ending up in horrible pain my first few days at home.

DK: I don't feel like there is a "worst," everything is a trade-off.

DS: The worst part of my experience was the unpredictability of it all. My story is nowhere near typical; my water broke at 34 weeks while I was on travel halfway across the country. My OB advised me to head to the nearest hospital, where labor was induced a few hours later when contractions had failed to start on their own. I had hoped for as natural a labor and delivery as I could handle, but after Pitocin, an epidural, and five hours of pushing, my son was delivered by emergency c-section and taken to the Special Care Nursery for respiratory distress. The first day of his life is a hazy recollection of feeling sick as a dog, seeing him attached to breathing tubes and IVs, and realizing that nothing was happening the way I had hoped, even in my more realistic visions. The lactation consultants in the hospital checked in on me what felt like hourly over the first few days, pestering me about whether I was pumping frequently and asking whether my milk had come in, making me feel like I was inadequate when I had to keep telling them no and wondering whether I was ever going to make any milk. When I finally started seeing colostrum on day four or five, the LC who came in next said, "Day four, right on schedule after a c-section," and I about let her have it for all the times they'd asked previously and made it sound like they expected anything else!

However, at least my son wasn't starving in the meantime. The attending physician in the Special Care Nursery was very conservative about feeding premature infants, so even though my son was rather large and had no breathing difficulties after the first 12 hours, the doctor wanted him fed intravenously at first and then bottle-fed very precise amounts, slowly moving up to my being allowed to nurse him twice a day, then adding more breastfeeding sessions, with no prediction of when we would be allowed to take him home. My son would gulp down whatever we were allowed to give him in a bottle, but he wasn't interested in latching on and nursing. Finally, a different lactation consultant came to visit us in the special care nursery and brought a gift with her – a nipple shield, which looked kind of like a sombrero made of Saran wrap. It suctioned to my breast and gave my son a silicone nipple more like a bottle to latch on to, and presto! He nursed like a champ. I had mixed feelings about the nipple shield though; as delighted and relieved as I was that he was now nursing and I wouldn't have to pump and bottle-feed forever, I was 1) annoyed that none of the other lactation consultants had tried this tactic sooner and 2) frustrated that I needed such an intervention (and a rather inconvenient one at that; it had to fit on just right, and it needed to be washed after every feeding). A few days later, with my son nursing better and better and gaining weight steadily, we were finally allowed to take him "home," which at that point was the hotel on the hospital campus. It wasn't until two days later, when we had flown halfway across the country, been picked up by my parents and spent the night at their house, and driven the two hours to our own home, that we finally felt like the ordeal was over and we could embark on the "normal" adventures of parenting.

EL: The pain. I have never had that much pain in my life. The hemorrhoids, the swelling, and the pressure (I was convinced that my vagina would fall out if I stood for too long).

JB: Loss of personal time and never getting one task completed.

JD: It quickly became clear why sleep deprivation is considered a form of torture. It hurts.

JM: Tie between emotional and physical fatigue. 'Am I doing this right? Is he hungry? Has he had enough to eat? Is he warm enough? Can he go outside?' and 'I am so tired. There is not enough sleep and massage therapy in the world to take this tired feeling away.'

JR: There were a lot of nights with little sleep, but this was not bad and to be expected.

KC: The initial depression I experienced after giving birth. At about the four to six week time frame, I experienced the "baby blues." It didn't last long, but it felt awful. I cried quite a bit – often for no reason. Instead of feeling more and more connected to my baby, I started to feel more distant. It was scary and upsetting because I'm usually a fairly happy and positive person. I was so embarrassed and didn't want anyone to know, so I tried to hide it and put on a happy face if I were speaking with anyone other than my husband or my mother. Thankfully, it was short-lived, and I do have an incredibly supportive, understanding, and patient husband who helped me through it.

KF: The sleep deprivation, incredibly sore breasts, the learning curve of soothing my baby. It's so hard to hear cries and not be able to comfort them away, but it really took weeks to get good at soothing.

KK1:   Being sick while trying to take care of the baby, especially while breastfeeding. No wallowing around in bed for me!

KP: I really struggled with the roller coaster of emotions postpartum. I would be happy, and then suddenly break out into a sobbing mess with little reason. I think my struggles with breastfeeding had a lot to do with that, but I think many go through the "baby blues" after baby arrives, and just don't expect it to happen to them. It has nothing to do with not being a good mother or not being happy with your bundle of joy!

KS: Lack of sleep due to nursing every few hours. It took a few months to feel normal again after giving birth and be able to exercise again to gain strength and energy back. That car seat is heavy!

LG: I was so clueless that I could not relax. Every guess I made about the baby was wrong. "She is crying because she is hungry..." "Uh, no she is crying because she is exhausted, and now it will be three times harder for her to sleep, silly!!!"

LK: PPD

LT: I had some trouble adjusting to life with a newborn at first, especially because my son didn't nap much at all when he was young. It was also very trying to be the sole person responsible for feeding him, at least for the first few weeks before we introduced a bottle.

MH: Self doubt. Worrying that I am not doing the best for my child. Being concerned that my desire to only breastfeed my child is causing him not to eat enough to grow strong.

RB: During the first few weeks, I had a ton of self-doubt. I was very worried about nursing and whether my daughter was gaining enough weight. She was totally fine, but that was a miserable stretch of time. Also, there were times when I wondered if I'd be able to love her enough, because in the midst of all the postpartum stress, it was hard at times to really connect with her. I felt a lot of shame about that until I heard from other moms that this was something many people felt. There were times when I'd wondered if we'd made a mistake having a baby, even though we'd done IVF to have her – which is so painful to write, but it's true! And I doubted if I'd really be able to take good care of her. Right now I can't imagine NOT having her in my life, but early on your emotions can really get you down. It was reassuring to know I wasn't the only one who had felt this way.

RO: The worry about everything, but especially childcare while I work.

SE: I was very isolated when I had my first child. I didn't really have any good friends who had had children. I was the pioneer of the lot. I often felt lonely and disconnected. I was jealous of my husband who went back to work and seemed to pick up his life where he left it, while I had quit work and was struggling to understand my lost identity and my new role as a mother.

SH: Lack of sleep!

SK1: It's tough losing sleep, but usually I sleep when she does when I'm worn out.

SK2: Feeling postpartum depression that led me to believe having had a baby was a huge mistake from which I just wanted to escape.

SP: There has been a lot that's been hard and bad. I'm not sure how to choose the *worst*. But I think that some combination of loneliness and feeling pulled in multiple directions by all the different types of parenting books is what has been the worst. Not feeling like I have a village helping me raise my kids. Or wanting more of one.

WC: The hormonal fluctuations and not feeling like myself for the first few months.

Kathy's Thoughts:

One message from all of these comments is this: Get your sleep!

For pain, some moms find that titrating down from narcotic pain meds to ibuprofen (600-800 mg) works very well. If the pain is interfering with your sleep, then continue one bedtime dose of the narcotic for the first two to three days. That can be useful.

Sheer exhaustion is more common than you think, whether it is mental or physical. Don't be reluctant to accept help. Get your partner to step in and provide relief. Nap. Nap. Nap.

To ward off any constipation caused by childbirth and narcotic pain medication, try magnesium tablets every day until you develop better regularity. Despite the urge to eat on the run and to swallow anything that tastes good and provides energy, commit yourself to build yourself back to a healthier diet. Trade at least one of those bagels for fresh fruit. Skip the pizza and have a salad. Then you'll feel like you deserve that chocolate.

For anxiety and adjustment difficulty, find a good therapist who will let you bring your newborn to the sessions. Look for someone who has faced some of the same stresses. In cases of depression, Zoloft is compatible with breastfeeding.

In general, lower your expectations for what you can accomplish at home with a new baby. Think of the job as one where you are just working to make more strides forward than back.

One Mistake You Can Save Others from Making

Question 8. What is the one mistake you can save someone from making?

We all have regrets in life, but mistakes that teach us a lesson are the ones that help us grow as women and mothers. No one wants to make a mistake with their baby. However, every honest mother I know can tell stories of dumb moves and egregious mistakes they have made. They joke about how it is that their children could have managed to grow into healthy adults.

Below is a list of situations that some new mothers hope they can help you to avoid. They aren't quite to the point where they laugh about it, but they know you can learn from their mistakes.

Mine? That could be an entire new book!

Breastfeeding

AB: I didn't take a breastfeeding class or do much research on breastfeeding beforehand. I was of the opinion that if it worked for us, great. I would advise anyone considering breastfeeding to speak with a lactation consultant or take a class beforehand. I hadn't realized that it doesn't come naturally for either the mother or the baby.

AT: Breastmilk may look curdled, but it isn't. Don't throw it out!

CB: Not all nipples are created equal…make sure you purchase the correct size equipment (shields, pump parts) for your nipples. Consult a professional! It will make your breastfeeding experience SO much more comfortable!

CK: Don't use a bottle.

HA: If you are breastfeeding, to not switch to formula if the flow isn't what you thought it should be. First, get the right pump. Then keep trying.

JB: Thinking that nursing is a quick job – it takes more time than you think.

JR: If you have to pump, talk to a professional to find out how long.

JD: Inform yourself about what you can do to build milk supply early on, and be very vocal in the hospital about your desires. Follow your instincts.

JM: Get a lactation specialist post-haste, if your intention is to breastfeed. Breastfeeding is not a natural and easy thing to do; professional help will make the process so much better.

KF: If your baby is crying, he/she is probably hungry. I wish I had realized that earlier. I feel like a big jerk for not getting it right away.

KS: Not taking a breastfeeding class.

LG: Get a lactation consultant on day one!

MH: Don't be afraid to ask for help. If you are struggling with breastfeeding your baby, call a lactation consultant. If after seeing the lactation consultant you still "don't get it," don't think you are dumb. That lactation consultant may not have connected with you in a way that was meaningful. Be willing to see someone else.

When you start freezing your milk, lay the bag flat in the freezer, which will make storing them a lot easier. You can use a narrow plastic container to store the frozen bags in chronological order.

As you are collecting bottles of milk in your refrigerator, use a dry erase marker to date the bottles, so that you know which is the oldest milk in the refrigerator.

If breastfeeding is very important to you, be sure to buy bottles that have a wide base and slow flow nipples that are similar to the breast. Eating from a bottle is less work than eating from the breast. You do not want to make bottle-feeding so much easier that the baby rejects eating directly from the breast.

MK:　If you plan on breastfeeding, take a class before you give birth and learn as much as you can then. It is so difficult to play catch-up after the baby is born, and in some cases, it can be too late.

OO:　Don't nurse your child to sleep.

PB:　Make sure to start pumping from the start in the hospital for stimulation.

RB:　I didn't ask about whether she might be tongue tied, and I wish I'd been more aggressive about that early on. If so, we may have been able get her problem fixed before she was four weeks old. Things are fine, but that's one thing I would re-do if I could.

SI:　Don't buy a pump. Wait until you know it will actually work for you. I have to use the heavy duty Classic at home and the Symphony hospital pump at work to keep my supply going. The Pump In Style never had a chance.

SK2:　Find an extremely accessible lactation consultant you can check with prior to taking any OTC meds, so you don't end breastfeeding before desired.

TT1:　For breastfeeding – Ask the hospital to weigh the baby more often and stand up for what you want in the hospital.

TT2:　If you plan to breastfeed, do your research. Know what to expect. Take a class and purchase the basic supplies before you have the baby, so you are ready to take care of business when the time comes.

Emotional and Physical

AC: Don't go rogue – make a plan and stick to it. Adjusting along the way is better than winging it.

BR: I really don't think we made any egregious mistakes that were earth shattering – maybe that's the thing I'd tell new parents as well. Just relax and know you'll make some mistakes, but it will all work out in the end. Read to your child, use common sense, and you'll be fine.

CV: I think making mistakes is part of the process, and there are so many ways to be a parent that I can't save anyone from anything, and if I could, I probably wouldn't want to. It's all part of the experience.

DA: a) TAKE YOUR PAIN KILLERS! You don't get any brownie points for being in pain, especially after a c-section. It took much longer to recover than I ever expected.

b) Trying too early to institute any kind of schedule. Especially when I was home on maternity leave, I didn't have any kind of schedule – why could I expect my child to adopt one? You can make yourself crazy with it, so don't try too soon.

c) Don't read all of the books. One will tell you this way is up and another will tell you it's down, and you will be confused, upset, and anxious. If you get to that place, take the book and hit yourself over the head with it because that's about how much good it's doing you.

DG: If things are hard and things suck, do something about it. Don't just assume you're doing something wrong, or that it is just supposed to be that hard. You don't have to suffer in silence. Trust your gut. If things are bad, there is probably something wrong. Trust your gut!!

DK: Nope – it's too individual. What I might view as a mistake, someone else might think is the best way to handle a situation.

DS: I'm sure I made plenty of mistakes, but I can't think of any that feel drastic or how to prevent them . . . just try to remember that there

116

are no magic bullets, so don't waste your time searching for them, and that babies are pretty sturdy little things, who will survive most anything their parents mistakenly do.

EL: Get the epidural if the pain is that bad – I waited far too long, and paid for it in the end, particularly after the birth. My baby was not drugged at all, and it allowed me to get that baby out vaginally. Act quickly if your milk is not coming in. Get lots of help when you first come home.

EM: I think just from assuming that it won't get better if motherhood sucks at first. The first few weeks were awful for me, and I was terrified that it might not get better.

HM: Eat good meals. Don't eat in front of the TV or standing at the counter. You are a human, treat yourself like one. It'll make you feel better. Sit down as a family, if possible. So much is shared around the table. Babies sit longer and are happier if they're together with the group. Make meals about the experience and less about the food. But enjoy the food – just know that they might not (definitely won't). Sing songs. Talk. Laugh.

JG: As soon as you are pregnant find out what to do/who to call if you have a pregnancy problem during the night. My doctor said that they don't bother people with that information until the pregnancy is 28 weeks in gestation. So going into pre-term labor at 26 weeks, I was oblivious about how to notify my doctor (it was a group of doctors) en route to the hospital.

KC: If you're a first-time mother and decide to attend Lamaze and other classes, use them as a guidepost only. Don't make the mistake of trying to follow their advice verbatim. Everyone's experience is different and everyone's body is different.

Our instructor stressed the importance of laboring at home until you're far enough along to avert a very long stay in the hospital. They provided strict guidelines to follow, in terms of how long your contractions should be, how far apart, etc. before you contact your doctor. Having had no experience with this, we followed their guidance exactly. Unfortunately, what they don't tell you is that it's possible your labor can accelerate very quickly. As did mine. We live minutes from the hospital, and yet, by the time we arrived, my contractions were already coming very hard and very fast. In the hour and a half it took for the nurses to sign me in and give me the required IV fluids and antibiotics, I had progressed from 3 cm to 7 cm and was in incredible pain. This might be fine for some, but I had planned to get an epidural and was becoming concerned I wouldn't be able to do that. Listen to your body and use the information you receive as guidance only. If you think you're ready, you just might be!

KG: I tell everyone I know to be more prepared to care for herself instead of focusing on the baby after birth. The baby showers, visits, and purchases are all for baby, and it's so key to get what you need done and bought for yourself, and to sleep, so you can become a good and happy mother.

KK2: In hindsight, I wish I had had the mental clarity to ask the doctor not to rupture my bag of waters; then we may've been able to back off the induction and resume at a later date, even if that meant hospital bed rest in the meantime. In essence, TRUST YOUR GUT!

KP: Everyone always gives the same advice: sleep when the baby sleeps. Sure, if you can do that, it's good advice. To me, I think the one mistake I made that I hope I could help others not make is not to worry about cleaning the house and doing dishes and keeping up with chores, etc. No one is coming to visit to see you or your home... they want to see the baby. They will not care if you have not vacuumed or dusted. Save yourself from the stress and learn early on that you cannot and do not NEED to do it all. Spend that time breastfeeding and building that bond...and supply!

KW: Don't skip that childcare class! I thought that by being an educated, 39-year-old, professional, experienced auntie of multiple nieces and nephews, I had no need for preparing myself for parenthood by taking a childcare class. I knew how to change a diaper, right? I had stocked up on everything I could possibly need in my nursery, right? I had skimmed the breastfeeding materials and would just see how it went... I would just jump in and swim...

Right? Wrong!

I realized once baby was home with me that I had no idea what I was doing, and no time to read those thick baby-care books I had purchased, but not made time for before I delivered the baby. As a result, my husband and I spent many hours flipping through those books and online searching for answers to our questions/issues as they occurred. I'm STILL reading those books now in my spare time and having "ah ha" moments left and right. I was horribly embarrassed at a visit with Kathy to learn that my child had a bad diaper rash and I hadn't known it. You mean it's not supposed to be that red? Duh?!

I'm going to chalk it up to narcissism. During my pregnancy, I read three entire books on pregnancy and delivery, and yet nothing about childcare since I couldn't see past my own physical changes and challenges. I was overwhelmed enough by the information at hand, by the thought of delivery, and by simply hoping I'd pop out a healthy baby. I wish I'd known to see beyond that and educate myself on childcare.

LK: Get help for PPD soon.

LT: Your labor will not happen like what you learn in class or read in books, so be FLEXIBLE!

MF: Discuss with your partner/husband how you are going to divide the chores and responsibilities before you come home with the baby. There is nothing worse than wanting to throw something at your husband for not getting up with the baby because you haven't asked him to. Men aren't mind readers.

MG: Don't think you can do everything you did before having kids. You can't and that is OK.

MM: Not sure. Everyone has a different experience. Just be easy on yourself – don't beat yourself up.

RA: Take a breastfeeding class BEFORE you are due.

SE: Don't over educate yourself. If you read too many books or are constantly looking things up on the internet, you are more likely to generate more anxiety than find answers to your problems.

SP: Don't lay yourself on the altar of mothering so completely that you fail to take care of yourself... and then one day wake up completely resentful, unbalanced, and depressed.

Baby Paraphernalia

AA: Please don't buy too many clothes for your baby because before you know they outgrow them.

BW: Schedule a car seat inspection early.

HM: Don't buy a bunch of crap right away. You don't need much of anything for a while. I know you'll have the urge to buy things and decorate and nest, and make it all perfect. But perfect is just two loving arms. I know that sounds cheesy, but it's true. Babies don't need fancy anything. In our culture, you'll feel pressure to get a lot of gadgets. But save yourself the clutter and the cost – just buy things as they become necessary. Trying to get a child to use something that is before their developmental stage is useless. They'll tire of it before they're ready for it. Just wait and see. Who knows – the very thing you need might not be invented yet! But it will right when you need it.

JR: Keeping too many items from your baby registry that you do not need. Try breastfeeding as soon as you get that baby in your arms. It is never too early to start trying. Your baby is awake from the big push, eventually it will want to sleep. It is great if you can take advantage of the awake time to give breastfeeding a try.

KK1: It's really easy to over-spend on baby stuff. Try to buy only the things you need at the moment because you never know what your baby will like or need during the next stage. Also, keep receipts and packaging!

RO: Don't buy too many diapers in one size. Those little bottoms grow fast, and poo escapes from diapers that are too small.

SI: Trying to recreate the hospital setting at home. I actually bought a super expensive acrylic crib from a medical supply shop because I couldn't stand that I may not be able to see the baby at all times from her bassinet. By the time it arrived, I couldn't believe I ever thought I needed that.

UG: Don't buy too many clothes, you will receive many, many onesies. And that's all they really need in the beginning.

SS: Make sure you find daycare early to be put on daycare waiting list!

WC: Don't get your couches cleaned before the baby comes because they'll be covered in spit up.

Kathy's Thoughts:

You can see how some of this advice contradicts what another mother has said... "read books" vs "don't read books." Maybe they meant "read the books with the answers you are looking for, but don't read the books that have the wrong answers." How do you know? You don't. The bottom line is that you need to know yourself and feel comfortable making your own decisions. With that comes the opportunity to both make mistakes and to have surprise successes. Don't sweat the mistakes.

> "Experience is the name everyone gives to their mistakes."
> Oscar Wilde, *Lady Windermere's Fan, 1892, Act III, Irish dramatist, novelist, & poet (1854 - 1900)*

Or as the boxer Muhammad Ali is reported to have said: "I'd rather be sorry for something I did than something I didn't do."

Favorite Gadget

Question 9. Do you have a favorite gadget you either purchased or devised?

For Baby

AC: Baby washcloths – folded twice to cover baby's penis while changing.

CK: I just bought it and haven't used it. But if the Nosefrida (the "Snotsucker") does what it's supposed to, it's going to be worth its weight in gold. My friends have used it when their babies were sick to "suck" the mucous right out of their babies' congested noses. It would be very helpful because congestion is the NUMBER ONE REASON my baby has difficulty breastfeeding when he is sick. And difficulty breastfeeding poses a risk to milk supply.

DA: a) Halo SleepSack with Swaddler. Know it. Buy it. Love it.

b) Any kind of baby-wearing device – you'll want both hands from time to time!

c) White noise CD/machine

HM: You can get by with a lot of cheap equipment. The IKEA high chair cannot be beat. That thing is cheap ($20), easy to clean, packs easily, is lightweight, and sits up to the table for older kids. It is amazing.

Also – buy things at thrift stores. You can get so much equipment there for so cheap.

CLOTH DIAPERS – Don't be afraid. They are easy and save you tons of money. It is not gross. Don't listen to your mother who did cloth diapers 30 years ago. They have Velcro and snaps and liners and great detergents now. You can do it. I promise!!!

JB: Diaper Genies and changing stations – one on each floor. No reason to run to the other floor.

JD: Diaper genie and a spinning drying rack for bottles.

JR: We like the Manhattan Winkle Toy, the Lamaze Catepillar, and Sophie the giraffe that is also a teether.

JR: Video monitor is a must.

KG: It's not a gadget, but Triple Paste diaper rash cream is truly amazing. My son got a horrible raw diaper rash as a result of an antibiotic he had been taking. After trying three other products that didn't provide any relief at all, I tried Triple Paste. His bottom was so raw that he would barely let me touch him and would scream when I tried to apply anything else. I applied the Triple Paste in the evening, and by the morning, it was about 75% gone. It was completely gone in about 36 hours. It's amazing and I plan to tell all new moms about it. You may not need it very often, but when you do, it's truly a godsend and will save your child a great deal of pain!

KS: Our baby was born in February, and almost every time we changed her diaper, she would pee. A friend suggested a wipes warmer, which we laughed at. But after breaking down (and buying one), she didn't pee or squirm anymore.

LK: Those swaddle blankets-for-dummies, things that Velcro.

MG: Any cooking tool is fun for the kids. Who needs toys? Everything in my kitchen drawers (besides knives) are toys!

OO: For my three-month-old, I think a mobile and a play gym is worth investing in – these items can occupy a child for 20-30 minutes, which makes it easier on a parent. In addition, I find these items educational for a baby.

RA: *Happiest Baby on the Block* CD. Helped us calm baby! We like our video monitor (helpful because we're usually downstairs watching TV in the living room while she's asleep in crib upstairs).

RB: The sound machine has been a life-saver! The ocean sounds are my daughter's favorite.

RO: I bought a Beaba to make baby food, and it's been worth its weight in gold.

RO: Diaper genie.

SE: Anything that puts baby to sleep! Swings, baby carriers, a stuffed sheep that plays white noise and sounds from nature, my glider.

SH: A large exercise ball. My son loves to be held in my arms while I sit on the ball and bounce up and down.

SI: Again I have two – the miracle blanket and the Brookstone sleep sound machine. The former got us a much needed four hours of rest when she was a week old. The latter lets us sleep now, as it makes white noise all night (most other sleep machines cut out at 45 minutes and would wake the baby).

Baby Carriers for Moms and Dads

AT: The Moby wrap. Great for babies who constantly want or need to be held.

HM: The Ergo baby carrier. It works for tiny newborns all the way up to heavy four-year-olds. And it won't hurt your back. You can get a baby on your back in two seconds by yourself and be on your way. It is awesome.

KK2: Baby K-TAN wrap.

TT1: The moby wrap.

KK1: I've used the Itzbeen timer more than I ever thought I would. It helps me remember what breast I last fed from and lets me know how long it has been since she ate. It also doubles as a completely mesmerizing toy – my daughter loves pushing the buttons and watching it light up.

KP: That ItzBeen timer thing was my lifeline early on, so I could keep track of elapsed time early on. Later, I learned to switch the wrist for the bracelet I always wear, so I can remember which breast I started nursing with during the last session. Wouldn't want them to get lopsided. :)

KW: My husband and I loved our "Itzbeen" timer. We received it as a gift, but you can find it at Babies R Us. It's a handy little timer that helps you to keep track of how long "its been" since you last fed the baby, put the baby down to sleep, and changed his diaper. It also has a "misc" item you can time, and we used it to keep track of when I last took my pain medication after my c-section. We were slaves to the Itzbeen during that first month when we were too sleep deprived to remember our names, let alone anything else.

RA: I really love the Candela nightlights I have by my bed. If baby stirs, then I grab one (it turns on when off the base, but also has a button on bottom to turn it off) and run into her nursery. It is dim, so it won't wake her if she's sleeping, but I can see her eyes open if she's awake. We can see what we need without the blinding bright lights of turning on lights... we can go back to sleep immediately. Candela Tooli, it comes with two (blue and green), and I've got one and my hubby has one on the other side. It looks a little like it has "ears," and those ears can be the handle you use by holding it between your fingers and still carry the baby and see where you're going. It is great!

SK2: Itzbeen was neat and might have used it more earlier on. So was the SMS feeder. The nipple shield was invaluable to facilitate a latch on a larger nipple for a month or so.

UG: Itzbeen. Records poops, pees, etc.

For Breastfeeding

AA: Definitely my breastpump.

BN: Hooter hider – it is brilliant!!!

CB: Nipple shield – baby can feed easier when you're engorged or pointy ;-), then just take it off and nurse comfortably on a fresh slice of bread!

CV: My pumping bra saved me! I could pump while using both hands for something else. This allowed me to hold Eliza and feed her supplemental milk from a bottle, hold a book and read, or when I went back to work, I could answer e-mails on my laptop in the lactation room.

DG: My pillow.

DK: Probably the Simple Wishes pumping bra.

DS: The Boppy.

EL: Love my pumping bra – allows me to pump and feed at the same time. Could not live without my Baby K-tan. That sling ALWAYS soothes my baby and puts him to sleep. With it, I can go anywhere, anytime, and know that he will be comfortable and quiet. I can also get chores done in the house easily.

EM: I really enjoy using a squishy over-sized purse as my diaper bag. This way, I can really use it as a pillow to sit the baby on while I breastfeed her away from home. I just sit with the purse in my lap and put her one top of the purse – it makes the perfect pillow.

JG: To ease the hassle of pumping in several places, I created a pumping box. I used a plastic box from baby wet-wipes. Inside that box I could fit all of my pumping supplies for my hospital-grade double breast pump. The little portion of the box that opens to release wet wipes was great because it would let air into the pump supplies, so they did not get mildewy or smelly.

KG: Bamboobies! (Nursing pads)

KP: Hands-free pumping bra... nice, but using hair bands to hook pump shields onto tank were a lifesaver early on!

LG: I loved my electric hospital-grade pump. Rent one regardless for the first two months.

LK: Cut slits in old bras to use as a hands-free pumping device.

LT: I couldn't live without my breastfeeding hands-free "bustier" that allowed me to pump very easily several times a day at work and at home.

MF: Too many to list! I love my Dr. Brown's bottle brush, my Boppy pillow, and my glider rocker the most.

MH: "My BreastFriend Pillow" made breastfeeding much more comfortable. It helped position the baby at the correct height. It also prevented my arms from getting too tired to hold him.

The "Simple Wishes" pumping bra made hands-free pumping a breeze. I am able to do other things while pumping because this bra keeps the pump secure.

MK: The hands-free pumping bra has changed my life! Now if they could only make that Medela Classic pump 20 pounds lighter...

MM: Manual breastpump helps me when I'm traveling.

RA: Love my Aiden & Anais Muslin Swaddle wraps: http://www.adenandanais.com/shop/swaddles.aspx

I used it for a light blanket, for swaddling her in the first two weeks (but large enough to still usenow – however, it stretches lots, so isn't going to really hold her well if she moves), to wipe her nose, and clean spit up. It is soft and breathable. I used it as a sun shield when out on walks with stroller and as a cover-up when breastfeeding in public. (It is breathable, so I can put it right over her head and have conversations with people who have no idea I'm breastfeeding.)I covered up with it while in one of the Smithsonian museums in DC, and the guard asked what I was doing in the quiet room that was closed to the public. I said, "I'm feeding her, a guard let me in earlier and said to let anyone know that he said it was OK for me to sit here while feeding." She replied with "Waiting for what?" I said, "I'm feeding her." She looked at me confused, so I pointed to the legs of the baby hanging out of the blanket, and then to my chest, and said "She's almost done eating and then I'll leave." She said, "OH 'feeding'! Take your time, sorry. You know you can do that anywhere... you didn't have to hide in here." I thanked her and said, "I really like the view of the national mall, so it was just fine for me here."

SK1:   Dr. Jack Newman cream, bra that holds pumping flanges.

SP: Hmm. I loved my nursing camisoles with the built-in bras. I never messed around with nursing bras. And I loved my Hooter Hider/ Bebe Au Lait.

TT2:   Simple Wishes hands-free bra. Pumping hands free gives you so much more freedom. You can read, write, eat, etc. while you are pumping. And it is adjustable for any size woman.

For Bottlefeeding

BR: When feeding the twins when they were infants and unable to hold the bottles on their own, we would place both boppies on the floor head to head (inverted parenthesis style). Then place each child on the boppies, so they're head to head. For each child, roll up a blanket and place it in a u shape under their chin and up on their shoulders and balance the bottle in that 'sling' position in the babies mouth. The head to head formation makes it easier for you to reposition (or replace) a bottle if it falls or becomes dislodged somehow. (*See Kathy's Thoughts on the dangers of bottle-propping.)

JM: Microwave steam bags to sterilize bottles and bottle accessories. Super-duper time saver.

Kathy's Thoughts:

Although it can be very difficult feeding twins simultaneously when you're home alone, I never advocate bottle-propping. I know this mother very well, and she never took her eyes off the twins for a second. Babies can drown with bottle-propping if left unattended.

Three Most Helpful Coping Strategies

Question 10. Name the three most helpful coping strategies you used after giving birth?

We all cope with stress in different ways. You can dive into the literature of sociologists and psychologists and come up with an infinite number of categories that have been coined to describe what people do and why they do it.

I tend to divide people into four groups when they have to get a result in times of stress. There are those who just buckle down and grind it out. There are those who decide to confront the underlying causes, get innovative, or make the job as positive an experience as they can. That might be as simple as finding some compensating rewards: go shopping, eat chocolate, read a book, or get a manicure. There are those who freeze, or who bail out mentally or physically. It might be just a temporary time out – we all know that one. And then there are an unfortunate few who lose their cool – usually at the wrong time or at the wrong people.

Each of these – even the last one – serves some kind of a purpose. No individual always has the same reaction to stress because there are so many factors at work.

Here are some suggestions that have worked for other moms. (However, I don't think you'll see that last option mentioned below.)

AA: 1. Take a nap whenever your baby naps.

2. Don't stress out to cook a meal/clean your house, rather get help from spouse/friends.

3. Talk to friends/other moms to get information.

AB: Deep breathing techniques learned in Hypno-Birthing. Closing my eyes and counting backwards from 1,000. Waking up every morning saying, "We can get through this day no matter what is thrown at us."

AC: Not having a scale in the house, getting out right away with and WITHOUT baby, and sticking to a routine.

AT: Accepting all help. Meditating. Taking each hour at a time.

BN: - Taking a hot bath by myself. I would give the baby to my parents or husband and take a bath for 45 minutes. I would read a book, call a friend, anything. It was me time. It also physically felt really good on my wounds.

- I joined a new mom group at the JCC. It was wonderful talking to moms in the exact same place I was in. Trutthfully, they were not people that will be my friends for life, but in those first few months—they understood exactly how I felt, and that felt good.

- After the first three weeks, I made it a goal to leave the house at least once a day. I made lunch plans, took walks (if it wasn't too cold), went to Target, sometimes only went to the mailbox. It helped to get out of the house.

- I also DVR'd TV during the day and watched it at night during feedings. It made me feel more positive about being up in the middle of the night if I knew I had an episode of *Glee* to watch.

BR: With twins, husband 50/50 involvement is a must – don't try to do it all yourself. It's your husband's parenting experience as well, so make sure he helps.

Accept people's offers to bring over food and (if they're family) to clean and just help around the house. You really have no time to do those maintenance things when you have infants.

Reach out to other mothers – not so great to talk to people with no kids about the recent breastfeeding. Helpful to chat with other women whose kids are in the same stage of development as yours.

BW: - Sharing my feelings and thoughts with my husband and listening to his supportive feedback.

- Positive thinking.

- Marveling at my daughter.

CK: The most helpful is meeting other new moms and planning regular playdates. Second is seeking information and help from professionals, such as LCs. And third is making sure my husband and I are working together and not against each other when it comes to baby care.

CV: Get out, ask for help, and drink some Guinness (or wine, but Guinness helps with milk production).

DA: a) We made a list of people we would let come visit us in the hospital, and it was short. We never said, "Stop by whenever you want to." We always picked a specific time for them to come, so we didn't have overlapping or back-to-back guests. This allowed us to have resting time and bonding time as a family, without constant outside companions, and we were much less exhausted in the hospital than other friends of ours who didn't do this.

b) Joining a new moms/first time moms group. Mothering can be very isolating. Finding a group of women in a similar situation is very important! It makes you feel less alone, less crazy, and more supported.

DG: My husband and I are well educated, masters-degree, upper middle class, older, etc. And I'm a very competitive person. So the way I coped was every time things sucked and I was crying, I kept thinking: stupider people than me have managed this. Stupider people have raised kids with no problems. If they can do this, I can do it better. Specifically, I thought about people I know who have babies (i.e., if Sascha can do this, I can do it).

Just being positive. When the lack of sleep or excessive crying was driving my husband and I crazy, I would force a smile, sing a stupid song like Journey or Vanilla Ice, and just love it.

Just accept that you're not perfect and it's okay to stay in your pajamas all day. Even if your mother-in-law is visiting. Oh well!!

DK: Due to the fact that my husband and I are both in our early forties, we decided to only have one child. We made this decision before I even got pregnant. Because of this, I made the decision to do my best to embrace every moment both because it goes by so fast and because being miserable was not going to change that stage/moment. When I was getting no sleep, I reminded myself that there would be a time that I would look back fondly on him being that size and I did not want to look back at it as a time that I was unhappy.

I also tried to keep in mind that fighting the situation (not getting sleep/him crying, etc.) would not change it – better not to try to swim against the current.

DS: Sleep. I slept as often as I felt like I could or wanted to in the first few weeks, which helped since I was only sleeping in 90-minute increments every night.

A moms' group. It might feel like a hassle to pack up your newborn and schlep off to some place with women you don't know, but there will be other new moms there, and they will give you friendship, encouragement, sympathy, and camaraderie that will make it bearable. If you can find one with lactation consultants on hand, all the better, so you can get expert help with nursing, as well as other women's stories and suggestions.

Prayer. I watched a lot of TV, especially in the evenings when my son would cluster feed for what felt like days on end (the Olympics were on when we brought him home, and I watched hours of winter sports I hadn't known existed prior to that), but I tried to spend at least some of each nursing session praying to restore my soul, center myself, and remember that I was part of something bigger than taking care of a baby.

EL: Giving bottles here and there (actually helped me to keep breastfeeding, as it was no longer all or nothing - gave me a much needed break), leaning on my relatives for breaks and naps, getting out of the house at least once a day or every two days.

EM: The one that comes to mind is having some free time or break time that is not used for napping. When things were really awful for me with breastfeeding, sometimes I would take naps during my "breaks" from the baby. When I did that, the time would go so fast, and I would awaken to a screaming baby and be right back in breastfeeding hell, without time to actually do something for myself. There were times that I would have felt more refreshed and renewed if I had done something I enjoyed – not napping, because I just felt so out of it when I got up anyway.

HA: Little bit of caffeine, though I try not to take too much (it was nice to learn that I actually COULD drink it in moderation while breastfeeding).

Ask for help and rely on my husband and parents when needed.

Try and schedule some time for yourself (e.g., get a haircut, go shopping).

HM: Sleep. I know that sounds crazy since that is the one thing you feel like you can't get. But I cannot emphasize enough the need to find sleep. Sleep deprivation will make you crazy, sad, and angry. It is not good for you or anyone. If you can, get a family member to come one night and get up with the baby, so you can get a full night's sleep. You might feel worse the next day, but you'll feel the benefit after that. If you don't have family nearby and no money, then take turns getting up and letting the other person sleep. You need it. There is no arguing this point.

Time to yourself. You need this, too. Go walk around the mall or paint or read or take a bath. Get OUT of the house by yourself or with friends. You need the break, and that is healthy and okay.

Communicate. Tell your spouse, family, and friends exactly what you need. They cannot read your mind. Don't think they'll get it if you're passive-aggressive. They won't, and you'll just be hurt and mad. Say it. I need water. I need a break. I need a foot rub. Go away. I want sex. I don't want sex. You know – all of it. Accept the help when it comes, too – just be specific about what you need. Please fold laundry. Please let me leave this house. Please

135

let me sleep. Please pour me a glass of wine. It'll make a world of difference if you just tell people. But be nice about it – you need them!

JB: - Get help from your mom and mother-in-law.

        - Split the chores with your husband.

        - Take a break. Showering is a good thing!

JD: (1)Ask for and accept help from others.

        (2) Figure out what absolutely has to get done and ignore the rest.

        (3) Forget what you used to think was important and take things one step at a time.

JG: Find a support network (friends, family, co workers, or all three), never say no to help, connect with a new mom's group or infant support group in your area.

        If you had a baby in the NICU, select a couple of people (staff or other parents) to stay in touch with as your child grows. These people have the best knowledge on your struggles.

        Also if you have a baby in the NICU, take photos or just note ways to measure the baby's size. This was a huge help for us to notice growth in just a week or two. Examples – take the father's wedding ring and see if the infant's hand or foot will fit inside OR use a CLEAN dollar bill and compare the baby to it. Check these things again in a week or two, and you will be surprised. This also gives friends a way to understand the size of your newborn.

JM: No coping strategies per se. I hunkered down with my husband, close friends, and family, all of whom helped me through the c-section healing phase.

JR: Go on a walk. Fresh air is great for you and the baby. You will likely find the baby will go to sleep in a carrier or in a stroller on walks. Know it is OK to pass on your child for any reason to an alternate caregiver. If you have neighborhood kids, have them watch your child for a couple hours a day while you are doing other tasks or out for a walk. This is a great way for them to learn to care for babies, and you get stuff done.

KC: Reaching out to discuss my questions/concerns/challenges with friends of mine – some of whom were also new moms and were experiencing many of the same issues in real-time, and others had older children, but had similar experiences. In many cases, it wasn't even the advice that was the most helpful, but, rather, the comfort of knowing that I wasn't alone. There were other mothers out there who had experienced the exact same thing and understood what I was feeling.

KF: I let people help me. Sounds crazy, but I don't normally let folks help me much, but I needed it! Sleep. Life is so much easier when I have some sleep. Comfort. I had so much discomfort that it really helped to do things to provide some comfort, including lots of hot showers and occasional massages.

KG: Getting meals delivered by friends, so we got some social time and nice home-made healthy food. Napping. Letting myself and everyone else off the hook for things.

KK1: I only have one: I told myself repeatedly during any difficult moments that IT WILL NOT BE LIKE THIS FOREVER.

KK2: Talking – aka – catharsis.

Walking.

Sleeping when possible.

All requiring emotional/friendship/family support.

KP: 1. Let yourself cry.

2. ASK for and accept help from others. You may have to bluntly ask for it, but do it. And ask for others to take care of the stuff that you don't have time for. You have time for the baby, so have them help with laundry or dinners or cleaning. You should be spending time with the baby!

3. Get out and venture back into public as soon as you can. Go shopping, meet up with friends, even go on a date!

KS: Support from husband and family. Cooking, cleaning, laundry, and suggesting naps when the baby slept. Organizing the babies' diaper bag for trips the night before and getting clothes out the night before. The mornings are too rushed.

KW: 1. Utilizing my network of family and close friends for venting my concerns and getting advice. It was helpful to know what they had also gone through and that I wasn't alone. I found that other mothers were particularly sensitive to my hormonal imbalance. They'd call to just "chat" and "see how it's going." Sometimes I'd end up crying through a phone call, as I was able to finally let loose my pent up feelings about my abilities and expectations. I'd feel much better afterwards...

2. I'm fortunate to have a very helpful and sensitive husband. He was my rock and my trusted teammate that first month at home with the baby and still is today. We learned through the experience that we made a very good team, and we're closer than we ever were before. Let your spouse share in the burden, and trust him/her with the care of the baby. You'll need a break. Communicate with your spouse about your worries, emotions, concerns, and questions. It is easier to work those things out together than alone.

3. Take advantage of the domestic help that is offered by friends and family in that first month at home. If they offer to bring you food, let them. If they offer to run errands for you, let them. If they offer to come hold the baby so you can shower, let them.

LG: Just do it. Take turns with the spouse at night with whatever you can.

LK: -Very hard to kill a baby.

-Laugh at least one big laugh every day.

LT: Letting the house "go," so to speak, and then hiring a cleaning service to help us out; letting myself cry at times, when I couldn't get my son to stop crying, telling myself it was okay, I was still a good mom; letting Alex learn how to put himself to sleep, even though it meant he cried for a bit when we put him down for a nap or at night.

MF: Deep breathing, crying when I needed to, and talking to my Mom friends who had been through the same thing.

MH: Be willing to share with your spouse/significant other what you need. He is likely more than willing to help, but needs to know exactly what you need. No matter how close you are to him or how sensitive he is, this is one area where he has no clue how to help. Be direct with him.

Sleep when the baby sleeps, but if all you really want to do is watch your favorite TV show, do that. You need to do what you feel will help you feel the most relax or rested.

Find a mommy and baby support group and start going as early as possible. Spending time sharing with other mommies at the same stage as you or a bit ahead will help you get through the transition.

MG: 1. Outsourcing things (cleaning, cooking, errands) that kept me from focusing on my kids and my husband.

2. Taking a walk with the girls every day.

3. Getting help so that I get more sleep (KEY).

MK: Sleep when the baby sleeps, eat and drink water as if you were still pregnant, don't try to do everything yourself – let others help you with the housework, errands, and cooking. There is no such thing as supermom!

MM: 1. Reading as much as I could on weekly developmental milestones and what to expect after birth.

2. Sleeping and staying hydrated helped me to produce milk.

3. Having prepared meals saved me time because cooking is out of the question the first few weeks you're home with the newborn.

OO: 1. Sleep when your baby sleeps.

2. Relax your "clean" standards in the house.

3. Keep in mind that all kids grow up, so you won't have to deal with certain challenges forever.

PB: I was not and am not good with this!

RA: Reminding myself that this was just a crying phase and to treasure how "simple" her needs are now before she grows up. While it didn't seem easy, I told myself it really was the "easy" phase, so relax and don't worry. The first few weeks she cried inconsolably – and I knew I'd learn what she needed and that she was safe, so while she screamed, there really wasn't much else I could do, but try to feed her and check her diaper and be sure she's not too hot/cold, so all I had left to do was love her and pray that tomorrow would be an easier day. It really keeps me calm. I'm told I'm a VERY relaxed mom, especially for being a brand new mom.

RB: a) Talking, talking, talking to other moms about their experiences.

b) Talking to my husband about what was going on in my head, so I didn't feel so alone.

c) Eventually, I started being kinder to myself and tried to stop beating myself up for "mistakes" or things I didn't know. I reminded myself that I was working too hard to be a good loving parent and that things wouldn't always work out or be perfect, but that I was trying my best.

RO: Talking to others (husband, mom, sisters, friends), sleeping, and taking some time to read (fiction - not books about parenting or childcare – those are not relaxing).

SH: 1) Tag teaming with my husband – when one of us has had enough, the other steps in to relieve.

2) Asking for help.

3) Talking to other mothers.

SI: - Chocolate. I ate tons of it.

- Being able to talk to my friends who kept reassuring me that what I was going through was completely normal.

- Having my mom stay with us for the first week. Even though we never needed to call on her expertise, it was so helpful to know that help was right down the hall.

SK1: Sleep, give your husband jobs so he feels useful, and give yourself a break!

SK2: Sharing feelings, concerns, and questions with other moms and professionals.

SP: Feeding myself, trying to get sleep, and leaning on help from my mom (who stayed with us after the births of the three girls).

SS: Talking to friends and family when you're about to LOSE IT!

TT1: Really, really sleep whenever you can. Stock up on nutrition bars and stash them everywhere.

Say no to visitors that aren't truly helpful. People who come should be able to just show up and do what needs to be done without any assistance.

TT2: Pump after you breastfeed to maximize your milk production and to give yourself a break from breastfeeding if you want to.

Find support. If there's a breastfeeding center near you, go. The sisterhood feeling is comforting. You are not alone.

Get out of the house. Whether it's to take a walk down the street or run a quick errand at the store, getting out of the house will lift your spirits and make you feel somewhat normal again. But don't overdo it!

UG: 1) Time-out sessions away from the baby. 2) Enlisting the help of those around me. 3) Not worrying so much about the housework, cleaning, etc.

WC: Making sure that I didn't isolate.

Joining PACE and an online first time moms meet-up group.

Staying in touch with coworkers and my boss, so the transition back to work wasn't so difficult.

Kathy's Thoughts

Short and sweet – Although I'd love to tell you that alcohol increases milk supply, it really doesn't. Having said this and knowing the research, I have some moms that still swear by it. The bottom line is... If you drink alcohol, be sure to wait two hours before breastfeeding your baby.

But there are no restrictions on chocolate!

Concerns Prior to Birth

Question 11. What concerns did you have prior to giving birth; what were your most afraid of? How realistic were those fears?

What we are afraid of in pregnancy is usually indicative of what we are generally afraid of in life. For example, the common pregnancy fears of "Will I know what to do?" or "Will the baby be normal?" or "Will the baby love me?" are all reflections about our doubts of our own competency, the fear of the unknown, and the fear of being alone and unloved. As our baby grows, our concerns sometimes grow too, and the more neurotic women are pre-pregnancy, the more neurotic, of course, they are during pregnancy. As with the rest of our lives, pregnant women need assurances from those around them that all will be okay, and if it is not okay, that the new mommy will have the resources and support to deal with whatever challenges arise.

When I was pregnant, I loved feeling like I always had a little friend with me, and I was never alone. I was making decisions about everything from what type of food to eat to what kind of music to listen to, with someone else in mind. It was amazing to me how strongly my choices were affecting another life. As I felt Adam and Erin wiggling inside me, I wondered, "What if I was making the wrong choices for this little one?" I was simultaneously vigilant and concerned throughout my pregnancy. As I read these responses, it's nice to know that I wasn't alone.

AC: Mostly fear of labor and vaginal delivery – had an unexpected c-section, so I had only 30 minutes, not nine months to work up fear over that. Yeah it was scary, but having my husband hold my hand made it all better.

AT: Having a c-section. Possible.

BW: I really didn't want to use drugs, but decided to be open to it since people seemed to think I was crazy for even considering delivering without drugs. I was mentally prepared, so I didn't need them, and I was happy I was able to do it without them.

CV: I didn't have a lot of fears going into my first labor and delivery. But because I had a 30-hour labor with a posterior baby and three suction attempts that ended in a 4th degree tear and 45 minutes of stitching, I definitely had fears going into my second labor and delivery just 16-months later. I really prayed a lot and trusted God to lead and guide the doctors, nurses, and my husband and me. I didn't want to elect to have a c-section, but I also didn't want to have another injury like the first. God answered my prayers because my labor and delivery with my son took less than two hours, and I had no tearing or drugs. It was amazing, empowering, and beautiful.

DK: My biggest worry was that I would have a c-section. I did have a c-section. There was no medical reason going into the birth for me to be a probable c-section candidate, but they are so much more prevalent than they used to be which is what caused my concern. It didn't end up being as a big of a deal as I had feared. I did feel that I missed out on part of the experience, but once he was there in my arms that didn't seem to matter very much, and within a week or two, it no longer mattered at all to me.

DS: I'm a little bit "crunchy," inclined toward things as nature intended, rather than as people invented, so from the outset, I was suspicious of the way the medical community treats childbirth. I was afraid of the pain, but I was also afraid of medical interventions that might hinder my body doing what it was intended to do. I didn't want an epidural, partly because it would make it harder for me to know when and how to push, but also partly (if I'm being honest) because I was totally sketched out by the idea of a catheter. I was afraid of being coerced into having a c-section I didn't really need, especially because I'm a diabetic who doesn't heal well, so having a large incision in my abdomen seemed like an exceptionally bad idea. As it turned out, all of these were somewhat realistic, although not in the ways I had expected.

The first hour of my labor was completely bearable, but as the cytotec and pitocin kicked in, the pain skyrocketed, and the epidural suddenly became God's gift to women. (I highly recommend them to anyone going through an induction, and I couldn't have cared less about the catheter. Plus it was nice not to have to get up to go to the bathroom in the first day after the c-section.) I did wind up having a c-section, and although many natural-birth advocates would have let me labor much longer, the labor and delivery staff gave me multiple chances to keep pushing and try different positions.

By the time the OB on call came in to tell me she really wanted to get me into the operating room, I had been up all night, pushing with every contraction for three hours, and I didn't have the emotional or physical strength to keep fighting – fighting the doctors for my ideal birth plan or fighting my body to give birth to a baby who never descended from -2 station. I was sorely disappointed that things didn't go as I'd hoped, but to this day I have a hard time identifying anything that I could have done differently to change the outcome, and as I healed well and my son is happy and healthy, I don't have too many complaints.

HM: I was afraid that by having a c-section I would miss out on the "normal" experience. And I was all worried about that part and sad (how it affected me). But the problem with the c-section turned out to be nothing to do with me – it affected my baby instead. She didn't get the fluid squeezed out and was in the NICU with fluid in her lungs and got fed formula and didn't nurse...etc. I never felt like I was missing out. You kind of forget about yourself when your child is in the NICU.

JR: No real fears, just not sure if I was going to have the quick birth or the 36-hour birth. I was very glad to have heard the range of stories, so that I knew all options would end alright.

KF: How realistic were these fears? My biggest fear was that I'd end up with a c-section. I ended up with a c-section. :) So, the fear was pretty realistic.

KP: I was terrified of having a c-section. I know it would not have been devastating if it happened, but I sure was glad it didn't.

KS: The birthing process and knowing when it was time to give birth. I ended up having an emergency c-section, so I was stressed out for nothing.

KW: I had a scheduled c-section due to the fact that the baby was estimated to be at least 11 pounds and have a large head. I was scared about the surgery and the hospital stay, as I'd never experienced anything like that. I was scared about the epidural and how I'd react.

I ended up having a very positive experience in surgery. I think I had been able to get to a very peaceful place in my mind prior to going in through meditation. I actually enjoyed the experience, as twisted as that may seem. I thought it was cool. I felt fortunate not to have to go through the pain and agony of a vaginal birth, even though prior to that I had felt disappointed not to be experiencing a vaginal birth. After the c-section I was like, "Hey, that was super easy – I feel so bad for those women who had to push for hours – ouch!" Don't get me wrong, I had some post-op pain. But I suspect it was nothing compared to pushing out a ten pound baby.

LT: Not giving birth naturally and how drugs would affect the birth and my son, particularly with his ability to learn to breastfeed; wondering how the doctors would react to my birth plan which asked for little medical intervention.

OO: I was afraid to have a c-section. I avoided it, thank goodness.

PB: I was worried about labor and delivery and how to know labor is for real. It was very realistic, although I made it to my induction date without going into labor, so it all went away.

SH: I was most afraid of complications during the c-section. The fears were not realistic.

SK1: I was scared of not being able to have a natural birth and that I would need an epidural. I am very proud of myself for having Camila naturally, but that short 24 hours flies by, and I am just happy she's healthy and happy.

SK2: That if I had a c-section I wouldn't feel (as) connected to the baby. I have nothing to compare my experience to, so not sure how realistic it was, but learned that a relationship with a baby is grown, and doesn't have to happen automatically or overnight.

SP: I was most afraid with our first baby's birth that I simply would not be able to push her out. I had dealt with vaginismus in the early part of our marriage (the involuntary clenching of the vaginal muscles, preventing intercourse entirely). And I was afraid that it would come back to haunt me, and that my body would not know how to birth. Birthing was incredibly difficult, but that had more to do with my anatomy, and really, nothing to do with clenching! For the twins, I had to have a c-section. I'd wanted very much to be able to deliver them naturally as well, but Baby A had been breech for weeks, so my physician was unwilling to consider it. I wish I'd known how difficult the c-section recovery would be.

UG: I was afraid of not being prepared with the right stuff or equipment, etc. Now I realize nothing can fully prepare you, you just have to dive in and do it. Someone once told me it's like constant on-the-job training.

WC: My water breaking on the metro. Fortunately, this didn't happen!

Physical Pain

AA: I was afraid of labor and if I would be able to take the pain. Well, when I was in actual labor, I was focusing on seeing and holding my 'lil' baby very soon and that thought kept me going.

CK: I was afraid mostly of the delivery itself... how painful it might be, whether the baby would be healthy, etc. In retrospect, I should have researched the birth less and researched breastfeeding and baby care much more. The delivery day is just that... one day... whereas the breastfeeding and baby care continues to be relevant on a daily basis.

DG: I was concerned about the pain. I watched a lot of Discovery Health and TLC baby shows, so you see all the horror stories. I was worried about the pain, so tried to cope by not thinking about it. Not smart. I didn't research breathing methods, natural birth coping, etc. Ultimately, my labor was super fast and fairly "easy," so I lucked out. As a result, I'd recommend women just avoid watching all those baby shows.

EL: The pain during labor and delivery. And yes, for me they were realistic. My labor was just as painful, perhaps more, as I had feared it would be. And I came dangerously close to having a c-section, another fear.

EM: I was just terrified of the pain of giving birth. I would tell people that the baby is like a ship in a bottle – it was pretty easy to get it inside, but something's gotta break for it to come back out. I planned on having an epidural from the start – but I assumed that everyone had an epidural. Based on that assumption, when people discussed the pain of childbirth I assumed that even with an epidural it must be excruciating. I was afraid of the pain. For me, it was shocking how not painful the whole experience was for me PERSONALLY. I had an epidural at 5 cm, and I really never had that much pain. It was great and now I won't be nervous if I ever do it again.

JD: I was probably most concerned about the pain of childbirth, and then I had a completely painless birth experience since I had a c-section before I really started contractions.

JR: Fear was labor, but I don't even remember the pain anymore.

KC: I was most concerned about the pain of childbirth and the lack of sleep once taking our baby home, and, unfortunately, I'd have to say both concerns were quite valid! I'd love to say that it was much easier than I had anticipated, but I'd be lying. Neither was insurmountable, but it was pretty painful while I was going through it.

KG: I was afraid of the pain of birth and worried unnecessarily about being sleep-deprived. They're real, but I found myself able to rise to the occasions to deal with them both when the time came.

LK: Pain, pretty realistic, but short lived – once I had baby, pain instantly stopped.

MG: I had two babies inside of me, and I just wanted them out, so they would stop pushing against my rib cage! I was also afraid there would be something wrong (health-wise) with them, but they are fine!

MM: Seriously, I was concerned my hemorrhoids were going to explode during the vaginal delivery. But I ended up having a C-section.

RA: Fear: Labor pain/preparedness of myself and husband/coach.

Reality: I ended up with a c-section before feeling contractions because her heart rate dropped and they said she'd have difficulties if I tried to birth naturally.

SI: - Afraid of childbirth. I ended up having a c-section because the baby was breech, and that was a breeze.

- Afraid that we would not bond. During the first few weeks, I was worried that we were not as close as we should be, but now I feel like my mini me is my little best friend.

TT1: That I wouldn't be able to handle the pain and that I'd have to get pain meds that I didn't want to take. I was lucky and had the natural childbirth I wanted.

Having a doula was so wonderful. She enabled me and my husband to not have the pressure of remembering everything we wanted to remember.

TT2: I was afraid of giving birth! I didn't feel ready to have a vaginal birth (e.g., would I know how to breathe correctly) and was thrilled when the doctor asked if I wanted a c-section. I jumped at the chance. Afterward I regretted it because I felt I missed out on the childbirth process and felt this hindered my ability to bond with my daughter.

Mental Preparations

CB: Get informed about c- section births if you know you're going to have one, or even if you're planning not to. You might have to, and it's helpful to be prepared just in case.

SE: Really just learning to surrender, take everyone up on every offer, especially for meals, cleaning, etc. When times are hard, don't allow yourself to become too self-critical. Times are hard because they are. Hard times come and go, so do good times. That's just the way it is.

With my first child I really wasn't that afraid of the birth, even though I was doing natural child birth in a birthing center with midwives – probably because I felt that I was young and strong and in good physical condition, and since I didn't have a lot of friends who had had babies, I didn't know what to be afraid of. By my third child, I had heard too many horror stories from other moms, and since I was having that baby in a hospital, I believed there was a greater chance of having a c- section or something else to happen. I prepared myself to be totally unprepared. Luckily, everything went fine.

Expectations For Help

MK: Neither my husband nor I have any family that live close by. I was worried that we would need help and have none. While I was definitely right about needing help, I am fortunate enough to have an amazing family who drop everything to come help when I need it most!

After Delivery: Breastfeeding, Caring for a Newborn, and Becoming a Mother

AB: Concerned that I wouldn't be a very good mother.

BN: I was afraid of how different my life was going to be and that I would never be able to just be me again, or have time with just my husband again. Those fears were very realistic. Life changes drastically, and it is impossible to prepare yourself for those changes. However, we have adapted and slowly I am learning how to take me time and how my husband and I can have us time.

HA: Balancing work, parenting, and school. It's crazy, but manageable so far.

JB: That I'd be a horrible mother. I'd constantly mess up with the baby. I was stupid. It's a learning curve and there are ton of people to help you when you ask.

JG: I had concerns about eating good foods for the baby. I think these fears were good for me as it kept me on a path of eating healthy.

JM: Shallow me: Will my body return to its former glory? Paranoid me: Will I drop the baby? What if I can't feed him? Diaper – how's that done now? These fears weren't very realistic at all.

KK1: I was afraid I wouldn't be able to breastfeed, and I was afraid I wouldn't be able to handle a crying baby. The breastfeeding could have gone poorly if I hadn't gotten help right away, but since I did, everything was fine. As for the crying baby – well, no one enjoys hearing a baby cry, but it's certainly different when it's your own baby that's doing the crying. All I want to do is make it better for her.

KK2: I was concerned about my baby's health, especially due to my two endocrine conditions. I didn't/don't want diabetes for my child. I was also afraid of induction/caesarean/the domino, afraid of things I didn't even have on my radar, and that I couldn't breastfeed. They all were realized except that baby's health is perfect.

LG: Afraid she would cry and I would not know what to do. Breastfeeding problems overpowered every single problem.

MF: You never know what your baby will look like, what kind of health he/she will be in, whether he/she will nurse, have colic, reflux, etc. Most of my fears went away once I had delivered my baby and saw that she was okay.

MH: My husband and I had virtually no experience with infants or babies prior to the birth of our son. I was afraid that my husband and I would not know what to do with our baby. A few weeks before our baby was born, my husband held a friend's infant. He seemed so nervous and awkward with him that I was worried he would be that way with our son. The nurses at the hospital spent time with us to teach us how to change a diaper, bathe the baby, and swaddle him. They also gave us materials to take home with us that ended up being like a little instruction manual. Almost immediately after our son was born, my husband helped the baby in the most natural manner. He seemed to comfortably be able to diaper, swaddle, and hold our baby.

RO: I was afraid that breastfeeding wouldn't go well. It was a challenge to get started, but I was lucky that my daughter has always been a good eater and she packed on the pounds like a champ.

SS: The concern I had prior to giving birth was how to efficiently do CPR on a baby. I am most afraid of someone harming my child at daycare. These fears are very realistic because they happen everyday.

Sleep Deprivation

BR: I always loved my sleep (and particularly sleeping in until 10:00 or 11:00 on the weekends) and was nervous about losing that. Unfortunately, my fears were realized and I do miss that – but on the upside, I don't sleep the day away any more.

Kathy's Thoughts:

Many moms find that their biggest fears are often unrealized. I believe the "worrying" prepares us to think through whatever comes our way.

Do Differently Next Time

Question 12. What will you do differently next time or what would you have done differently if given the chance?

This chapter is about getting a mulligan (a second chance) – and giving that opportunity to someone else before they do something to need it.

Preparing: Body & Mind

DS: Oh . . . if given the chance, I'd have my next baby at a birthing center that would give my body a little more time to get through the birthing process on its own, but as a high-risk pregnancy, that's not an option. I think that next time I will try to be more mentally prepared (early, as I have an increased likelihood of preterm labor again) for labor and delivery, but I will also have less expectation that I can predict or control what will happen. Just like you can't fully prepare someone for all the ways that having a baby will change their life, you can't have a contingency plan for every possibility during childbirth; there are some things you just have to roll with.

EM: I would have tried to rest more the week I was due. I had heard that first babies are always late, that first-timers go to the hospital only to be sent home over and over again. Therefore, I assumed that I'd have plenty of time for sleeping because labor would come on so slowly. It wasn't like that for me, and the biggest mistake I made was not going to bed super early when I felt the first very mild contractions. They progressed fast and I ended up not sleeping much at all before my labor.

JG: 1. Find a doula to be at the birth.

        2. Tour the hospital where you will be giving birth, and find out what to do if you have problems after office hours.

JM: Next time, I would take my own advice about making a list of tasks for family and friends who want to help. Didn't do it before the birth of our son and spent lots of time trying to remember that thing I needed done....

KG: Breathe. Trust in the natural processes. Ask for and accept help.

KS: Nothing, I did a lot of prenatal yoga and pilates, as well as cardio during the pregnancy. I believe that played a big factor in the quick recovery.

MF: Not wait so long to have a baby. It's the best thing I've ever done.

MK: I thought I was pretty well read on what to expect, but there was a lot of information that I didn't know, particularly about breastfeeding. I would definitely have learned as much as I could have about breastfeeding beforehand if I were able to do it again.

MM: I wish I was at a more ideal weight prior to getting pregnant (opposed to being obese according to BMI standards) and that I was not pre-hypertensive prior to the pregnancy. I wish I did not stress over things I could not control and said 'no' to people earlier during my pregnancy.

SK1:   I might have gone to a support group or La Leche group early on.

SS: Working out more and watching what I ate. I got caught up with "eating for two" and got HUGE.

The Delivery

AA: I would have taken an epidural a 'lil' earlier (say when I dilated 4 cms and not wait till 6 cms).

BW: Next time, I want to find out more about how I can have a better recovery. Also, find out if there are any pain management options for immediate recovery after a natural delivery.

EL: Get the epidural MUCH earlier (I waited seven painful hours).

JD: I would spend more time with the baby right after she's born if at all possible.

JR: I would ask another person in the delivery room, NOT ME, to take a photo of my husband cutting the umbilical cord. I thought I had it, but I just couldn't get the angle, and then the moment was gone. I am sure the nurses would have snapped the shot for us.

KK1:   I will ask for a different nurse if the one I have during labor is not helpful. The horrible nurse I had during the worst part of my labor made everything so much worse than it needed to be.

LT: I would not check into the hospital until I was well past 2-3 cm dilated (I ended up checking in at this point, and Alex wasn't born until over 24 hours later!) and minimize the interventions (i.e., not letting them break my water unless absolutely necessary). I will still hold out for a natural birth the second time around. I was happy to only need the epidural for a few hours for the first time with Alex.

RO: I think that next time, I would be more vocal with the hospital staff during the delivery. There was a lot going on with my daughter right after she was born, and unfortunately, I was numb from the waist down and physically unable to get up and be next to her while it was going on. I wish that I could have had more control of the situation, even just keeping them from giving her a bath in the first couple of hours after she was born. There was no need for that, and I didn't know how to stop them. I feel more empowered as a parent now, so next time I'll yell across the room if I have to.

TT2:   If given the chance, I would have made every effort to have a vaginal birth.

CK: With my second baby, I will do all the above that I've mentioned, including making sure s/he takes a bottle. I haven't decided whether I'm going to co-sleep again, as I did with my firstborn. I loved co-sleeping, but it's been a difficult process sleep-training my son.

HM: I wish I'd been more forceful with the NICU staff about letting me breastfeed or pump. I wish I'd known my rights. I wish I'd made my voice loud enough that I couldn't be ignored instead of worrying about "making a scene." I'm sure that her being in the NICU and not nursing was not the only thing that affected our experience, but it didn't help.

LK: Gotten help sooner for PPD.

PB: I will ask for a pump ASAP at the hospital. I also will not see their lactation consultants who just shove the baby on you constantly and get the baby so worked up that they then refuse.

SE: After my first child, I wish I had sought some kind of couples counseling to help us both "readjust" to our new relationship. There is really not enough info out there about how a baby affects you as a couple. We had just gotten married when I became pregnant, so we hardly knew ourselves as a married couple, let alone parents. You now have a whole new identity as a mother, and so your relationship changes. It has a new identity, too. There is not a lot of focus on what the partners are going through. Partners often feel very overwhelmed, helpless, and useless, but are less likely to be educated on these feelings and how to cope with them.

SP: I don't have a lot of regrets, but I do wish I'd made more time for myself, and beat myself up less. I wish I could have felt less guilt! (This is still something I struggle with, so I should probably start trying to take this advice now.)

WC: I would have rested more during the first few weeks. I went out a lot, and I should have relaxed more. I just wasn't used to staying around the house so much.

Feeding

CK: With my second baby, I will do all the above that I've mentioned, including making sure s/he takes a bottle. I haven't decided whether I'm going to co-sleep again, as I did with my firstborn. I loved co-sleeping, but it's been a difficult process sleep-training my son.

HA: I would have changed the breastfeeding technique.

KW: I would have had Kathleen McCue come in for a lactation consult on day one :).

MH: I would have seen a lactation consultant as soon as I got home from the hospital instead of waiting until the breastfeeding had gotten virtually unbearable.

TT1: Give formula earlier to avoid the large weight loss, which resulted in having to wake the baby every 2-2½ hours for three weeks, so she could get back to her birthweight.

Practitioners

AT: Go to a birthing center, rather than a hospital.

KF: I probably would have done more research on doctors/hospitals in advance of getting pregnant. I may have still used the same practice, but I was so attached to my practice by the time that I had a successful pregnancy (I miscarried four times) that I didn't want to consider other doctors. I wish that I had though.

KK2: I will see same doc/ob throughout, but a different perinatologist (less invasive). I will take more time off work. I will challenge any recommendations for induction, unless clearly needed... If given the chance, I wish I could've gone into labor organically and birthed at home, attended by midwives. I'm a candidate for and am praying for a VBAC (vaginal birth after c-section) ... when/if there's a next time.

KP: I would have changed pediatricians right away when I felt scared about going! I remember sitting on the floor one night bawling because I was scared the pediatrician was going to yell at me because the baby didn't gain exactly what she expected. I felt like I was going to the principal's office to be reprimanded. You choose your pediatrician. You need to be comfortable with her and all in her office. I wish I had moved sooner, but it's never too late. She needs to see eye to eye with you or it will never be a good match.

OO: If I am pregnant again and want to have a natural birth, I would try a birthing center this time instead of a hospital.

SI: - I would have gone to a different OB. He was very relaxed – which I thought would offset my type A personality, but instead it made me feel that he was somehow incompetent.

- I would have learned more about breastfeeding prior to the baby's arrival.

- I would have pumped more, breastfed more, and taken more time to sleep.

Maternity Leave

BN: I would have left the baby with someone else more before going back to work. The only time I left the baby in the first 16 weeks was once to go get gas and once to go to the grocery store. Going back to work was very rough because I did not build up to it.

DG: If I could have done something differently, I would have planned my work "exit strategy" to account for an exit at 37 weeks (or even 35), instead of the 40 week due date.

Also, next time I'll know what labor feels like. First time, I was just unprepared because I didn't know what to expect.

RA: I would have learned how to recover from a c-section. I would have set up more help at home had I known I'd have a c-section (like order foods to be delivered and ask for mom to stay two weeks, or set up friends to cycle through to help me physically). A post-partum doula would have been ideal for me I think and I might actually hire one next time.

Tell everyone to take a breastfeeding class before delivery if they plan to breastfeed.

General

AB: Not eaten the spicy calamari salad that caused my water to break 16 days early. Be prepared that a baby can come at anytime. The baby does not get the memo to be born on the due date.

BR: Don't be too quick to get rid of the high chairs – we got rid of them before they turned two years old and that may have been a bit early. Complicates things in a restaurant because they always wanted to be on my lap, and then it's impossible to eat! On the upside, you'll likely lose some weight.

LG: I was so clueless that there was no salvation for me. The best thing I can do is just think that now I know better and I look forward to the next one. If I had to do something differently, it would definitely be to try to relax and enjoy the experience more.

RB: I would like to think that I'll be easier on myself! And just accept how I feel and not feel guilty about needing/wanting breaks and/or not immediately knowing what to do about every issue that crops up.

SK2:   Not sure, won't know until I see how baby turns out – seems fine enough now, so not willing to second guess choices made.

Great Bottom Line Advice

AC: Relax.

Kathy's Thoughts:

I have a funny saying "You don't know what you don't know until you need to know it and realize you don't." Unfortunately, in order to learn something important, we sometimes have to make mistakes first. We don't really confront the situation until we find ourselves at an important crossroads and have to make a choice about which path to take, knowing that the decision might not be so easily reversed. Sometimes the decision leads to unexpectedly great results. Then you find out that "you knew what you needed to know, but didn't know that you knew it until you needed to know it."

The purpose of this book is to help give moms some ideas of what may be important to consider prior to giving birth and breastfeeding.

Relationships with your obstetrician, midwife, lactation consultant, pediatrician, nurse practitioner, and doula are all especially important. You will need to partner with these people during some of the most important times of your life. Take the time to find people you can relate to and that share your principles and basic ideas. You may have to interview more than one or two practitioners in each specialty. The work to find an ally can be daunting, but the rewards are great. You'll just know a person is the right one. And then your relationship with them can be happy and lasting.

Things Spouse, Family, Friends Did That Were Helpful

Question 13. What did your spouse, family, and/or friends do that were extremely helpful?

We can all learn how to help each other by reading these suggestions.

Food and Household Chores

AT: Hold our baby and cook for us.

BN: Cooked, cleaned, did everything else that I normally do. I just had to be there for the baby.

DA: Bring food over for us, but did not expect to eat with us.

Take photos of our entire family.

DK: The people that brought food and other essentials – they saved us!

EM: My friends brought food, loaded my dishwasher, washed their hands before holding the baby without being asked, asked how I was doing.

JB: Bring food, clean house, walk dog.

JD: Friends and family provided meals and frozen food for future use.

JR: Meals.

KG: Laundry, dog walking, dishes, guarding the quiet zone so I can sleep, bringing over food.

LK: Brought meals, fed baby during night occasionally, brought baby to me in the night for me to feed.

MG: Took the girls so I could sleep. Cooked meals; left food in the freezer for after they left; cleaned the house. Didn't judge us or give us unsolicited advice. Lent us things they didn't need anymore.

MK: My laundry! My dishes! The cooking! The housework! I was in no shape to do any of that after giving birth, and it was really nice to have a hand.

PB: Helped with food and cleaning.

RA: *Friend didn't take "no" for an answer and dropped off a rotisserie chicken for us the second day we were home.

*Mom – stayed with me for first week (needed two weeks, though). I just sat on couch/bed shirtless trying to feed baby and recover from c-section. Mom would bring food/water to me or hold baby while I went to the bathroom. She went to store and cooked/cleaned all week. I couldn't have done any of those activities and would have not eaten enough (or anything) if she weren't there, and thus would not have had energy to breastfeed.

*Other new moms or aunts would cheer me on when I said breastfeeding was too hard, I was frustrated. They'd say "yep, normal," and they suggested foods/tea to help milk production and reminded me to eat/drink enough. They told me what "must have" products to buy for baby (like a swing and *Happiest Baby on the Block* book and good nursing bras/tops, etc.), which made me feel like I wasn't alone or isolated. Just having people reach out with "been there, done that, yes – you can!" really helped me in my "fragile" state.

SE: Make meals, run errands, and do laundry!

SH: Cook meals for us, as we had no time/energy for cooking.

WC: Friends and family dropped off food. We didn't have to cook for two weeks; this was a huge help.

Baby Gifts

MM: Bought items for the baby. It is very expensive to try to buy everything yourself. Don't feel bad using Craigslist or accepting hand-me-downs from family or friends. As long as they are in good to new condition, it's okay. I don't recommend buying used breastpumps or carseats.

Emotional Support

AC: Let me have the spotlight.

KC: They listened. One thing I really appreciated is the fact that my friends usually didn't offer advice unless it was clear that's what I was asking for – because sometimes I wasn't. Sometimes you just need to talk and you don't really want someone telling you what to do or trying to solve your problem. Most of my friends were already moms, and they really seemed to appreciate the importance of listening and empathizing. That's not to say that I didn't want their advice. I accepted advice on a variety of topics... but sometimes I just wanted to talk to a friend.

KK2: Tried to humor all my requests; took care of me.

LG: My husband helped me get through the depressed mood I suffered due to not being able to breastfeed. He listened to me and encouraged me. He took me out for walks.

OO: Be there for me and help as much as possible.

SK2: Listened, accepted, were empathetic, shared similar experiences, seemed not very judgmental. Gave feedings, held the baby. Husband still allows me extra sleep on weekends!

TT1: Support me in whatever decision I made/whatever I was feeling, even though that changed regularly sometimes.

Unique and Miscellaneous

JG: One friend signed us up for www.foodtidings.com website and people just started signing up to bring us dinners.

My spouse set up a caring bridge website and added photos or a journal entry to it everyday. That way, we were able to let everyone know what was going on with our son in the NICU. It relieved me of calling people back and having to talk about the same thing fifty times.

SS: They came and visited me and stayed for a week or so. They stressed and assisted me with keeping proper diet while breastfeeding, as well as giving me time to do things for myself.

Spouses, Grandmothers and Close Family Members - YAY!

AA: My husband and mom took care of my baby for the first month when she was awake. All I did was Breastfeed her and take rest.

AB: My mom stayed with us for the first month and handled much of the night feedings. I was exclusively pumping, and having her feed the baby while I pumped in the middle of the night kept me going. Otherwise, it's easily a two hour process in the middle of the night – you can easily convince yourself not to pump; unfortunately, you can't convince a baby not to eat.

BW: My husband talked me through the delivery by talking about good times we've had together and holding my hand. Afterwards, he's given me massages and took care of making meals and doing housework. Also, he's been really supportive and sweet.

Family helped out by stopping by with lunch and dinners and helping with our dogs while we were at the hospital.

CB: Grammy came and took baby number one out of the house while I nursed baby #2. Church group brought meals twice a week. Church Grandma came over to hold new baby for two hours while

I got a nap. Get someone to come stay with you or come over daily!!

CV: My mom came, even though we originally planned to be on our own the first week. She was the reason I ate, wore clean clothes, and rested in the early days. She was amazing because she stayed in the background and just did whatever needed to be done, so that we could take care of the baby. The second time, she was here to entertain our older child, while we dealt with our newborn. There is nothing like your own mother in this particular time of need.

The best help anyone – family or friend – can give in the beginning days and weeks is to ask how he/she can help. Some moms might want to be left alone, so they can figure it out. Others might want a meal or help folding laundry. Still others might want a visit to get a feeling of "normalcy" and life outside of baby. Some might want you to babysit for an hour, so she can run an errand. Just ask.

DG: My husband also took leave. I took 16 weeks, and he took 12 weeks, so we didn't have to worry about childcare until our baby was almost seven months. It was much easier to part with her at that age than if we'd had to do it when she was three months.

DS: My husband was wonderful at trying his hand at everything (diapers, baths, etc.), even though it was all brand-new to him. My friends from church set up a dinner service and brought over meals every night or every other night, which usually gave us enough for leftovers at lunch as well, and gave me some very practical, necessary relief. (In fact, two weeks after we got home when the "service" was over, I had a mild anxiety attack about what we were going to eat, until I reminded myself that I had been cooking for years and could figure out how to feed myself! Even if the first meals were all simple slow-cooker recipes.) My mom came down for a few days and cleaned my whole house, which was amazing.

EL: Spouse – helping with night feedings, putting the baby to bed, getting dinner.

Family – holding the baby to give us rest time, helping with feedings, cleaning, shopping, food preparation and laundry.

HA: My parents have taken care of my baby for a few weeks so that I could go back to work and she could delay going to daycare.

HM: My sister would come and just set straight to work with all the things around that needed to be done – the laundry folding or the dishes. It was such a huge relief to have her come. Our neighbors brought us meals for weeks after the twins were born, and that was such a tremendous blessing.

JM: My husband took six or eight weeks off work (I can't recall exactly). We were in it, all of it, together.

JR: My mom did not just descend. She asked when we thought her visit to see the baby might be most helpful. She came two weeks after when my husband returned to work. When she was here, she made a lot of dinners to freeze. It was very helpful in the moment and for the future.

KF: Mothers stayed with us and helped with cooking, cleaning, and provided baby backup. My mother never placed pressure on us to hold the baby, and I really appreciated that. I really wanted to use her as backup, but try and do things myself, so that I'd feel comfortable when it was just me and my husband taking care of him.

KK1: They fed me. My mom was especially helpful since she knows what I like and didn't even have to ask me what I wanted. She'd just show up with good food.

KS: Spouse was super amazing and helped with cooking, cleaning house, washing bottles, changing baby, feeding baby (Need I say more?). It made the first few weeks much easier to focus on taking care of the baby. Friends and family would come over and bring food and help with laundry, which seemed to double.

LT: Spouse did everything besides breastfeeding, so he changed baby, took him after feeding for burping, changing, or just to hold while I rested. Also put baby down for sleep. Mom did same thing, as well as stayed three days/two nights/week and got up with baby after I nursed him. Also did laundry and made dinner and did dishes. Friends came to visit and brought food.

MF: My husband was wonderful after the baby was born. He jumped right in and started changing diapers, holding, burping, feeding, etc., right away.

MH: My husband planned ahead for the time that he would be back at work and I would be home with the baby. He made sure there was food in the house that I could easily heat up and/or eat so that I didn't have trouble eating while I was alone with the baby. Friends came or sent food to the house.

RB: During the first few weeks after my unplanned c-section, my husband took on everything but nursing. He took care of diapers, laundry, etc., so I could focus on nursing and healing. After he went back to work, he'd make lunch for me at night, so it would be easy for me to grab food during the day. And he kept his sense of humor, which was very helpful!

My sister kept telling me that everything will get better – nursing, sleeping, napping, etc. Over and over again, she would tell me that things would get easier. I clung to that during those first crazy weeks. And she was right.

Our family and friends brought a lot of meals by, which I think was the most helpful thing they could have done. When they visited, they didn't stay long either, which was also helpful.

RO: My husband took four weeks off from work when my daughter was born, which helped us establish our new routines and get used to being a family. We also had other family members come in turns to stay with us and help out. While no one else can breastfeed for you at 3:00 am, it was nice to have help around the house. My sister spent a weekend cooking for us and freezing meals, which was amazing. I wish she would come back! I also had two friends who had babies around the same time, and for both of them it was their second. They have answered probably a million questions (and counting) and are always up for a conversation about baby minutiae.

SK1: My husband took over cooking and preparing food. That was the best. He would also be the errand boy and do all the shopping. He just has a more flexible day since I'm breastfeeding every two hours. When my mom was around, she brought leftover food for us to freeze and eat whenever and she also cleaned.

SK2: - My husband stayed with me the first two weeks.

- My mother stayed with me the first week.

- My friends brought food and stayed for no more than a half hour.

- My mother hired someone to clean the house for me and to cook once a week.

TT2: My husband took care of the baby every night so I could sleep. Since I was pumping, he could give her as many bottles as she needed, and I could get five to seven hours of sleep every night.

UG: My family helped with meals and housekeeping. They also went to the grocery store and ran errands. My sister-in-law was great for emotional support, especially with the trials and errors of breastfeeding since she has two kids of her own.

No Help :-(

KP: I wish I could tell you this, but I was so focused on being Super Mom and managing everything myself that I didn't LET anyone be helpful. Not that anyone asked really, but I probably would not have let them anyhow.

Kathy's Thoughts:

There is a lot of great advice here. You should think about what resonates best with you. Once you have an idea of what you think will work for you, talk to your family. Let them know what you anticipate you will want or need. If you find that your expectations change, and the game plan changes with it, just adjust as needed. And be sure to let your family know – so they won't be surprised. (Also, it might save them from a purchase that would have met your initial needs, but that doesn't fit your revised game plan.)

It would not surprise the other moms who have related their stories here if a fundamental challenge for you is simply whether you can accept help. No one wants to be needy, but this is one of those situations in life where asking for help and giving it is a win-win proposition for you and for your friends and relatives. Don't let it be difficult. Enjoy it, and let them enjoy it too.

I usually discourage having too many visitors in your home early on. Close family and very close friends may be the exception. One rule of thumb is that if you can't walk around in your post-delivery underwear or be breastfeeding while they're sitting there, then they probably don't qualify as close enough, and you should let them wait a week or two before they come over.

Things Spouse, Family, Friends Did That Were Not Helpful

Question 14. What did your spouse, family, and/or friends do that weren't so helpful?

The main categories of responses are:

- They expected too much.

- They did too little.

- They said stupid things.

- They actually did something good.

Here's who's responsible for all of this; the categories are occasionally blurred, as many moms reported on several people in each response.

Maternal Grandmother

EM: My family pretty much ignored me after labor and only wanted to hold the baby. A week before I was due, the women in my family told me I should do all kinds of things to induce labor. They told me I was "emotionally" holding on to the baby – an entire WEEK before I was due. My mom offered to hold the baby while I cleaned my house about a week after the birth – that wasn't helpful. My

173

parents were inconsolably offended at being asked to wash their hands before holding the brand new baby. My mom tries to make me cover up while nursing in ways that are uncomfortable for me and the baby – all unhelpful.

HM: My mom always wanted to hold babies and let them sleep on her. This was not what I needed at all. It's hard when family members don't respect the schedule you're trying to keep, and nothing can be addicting to a baby like being held to sleep. It's fine in the beginning, but it's a slippery slope. And if you're trying to get the baby to self-soothe and other people have trouble letting them fuss and pick them up, it's counterproductive. Be specific about what you want. And if you're a family member – follow the instructions. Yes, you have been a mother for 30 years. But it's her turn now – respect what she wants.

SK2: Mother suggested I do as she did – go back to work prior to three months off – escape into work.

In-Laws

DS: Offer unsolicited advice. Everyone wanted to tell me their stories, most of which had no bearing on what I was currently going through (very rarely did anyone ask any questions to figure out what I thought, what I had tried, or anything else that might have been relevant at the time). It made me annoyed when folks who hadn't had children in a long time wanted to tell me about what their kids did, but it made me absolutely nuts when people who didn't have any kids wanted to give me all kinds of suggestions, gleaned from observing children in restaurants or watching their nieces and nephews once in a blue moon.

On the other end of the spectrum was "I'm not going to do or say anything," which was also unhelpful. My mother-in-law came down for a long weekend and spent 95% of her time sitting in a chair reading novels. I think she was waiting to be told how to help, but then she had to be walked step-by-step through even simple things like cleaning the kitchen, which I had no more energy or time for than I did for actually cleaning. I wished that if she was going to be in my house, she would take a little bit of initiative to notice what was going on around her and step in from time to time without taking over or being intrusive. It felt like we needed to take care of her almost as much as we needed to take care of our newborn, which was an added stress we really didn't need.

JG: The first visit when my in-laws came I ended up preparing several meals for them, which was incredibly frustrating. I understand that my husband needed pampering from his parents (having a child in the NICU for months was taxing on us both), but I was in no mood to cook for guests. After they left, I told my husband that was never to happen again, and it did not happen again.

KC: My in-laws were a little too involved in the early stages. I needed some space to figure things out, hold my baby, and just navigate being a new mom. They wanted us to visit every weekend, and almost as soon as we'd get there, they wanted to take my son out of my arms to hold him. Although I understand that it was only because they loved him, it felt very intrusive at the time.

Also, a few family members did provide some unsolicited advice a couple of times that wasn't necessarily welcome. There's a fine line between helpful advice and criticism, and even with the best of intentions, some have a way of navigating that sensitivity better than others.

KG: Mom-in-law came to visit and expected to be cooked for and driven places, so it wasn't a help whatsoever.

KW: It was difficult to have our family come to visit on week two after the baby was born. They had good intentions, but just didn't know how to help me the way that my husband could, and I felt awkward asking them for help because they were my in-laws. My husband had opted to go back to work that week, while his family came to stay with us, thinking they would fill the void. However, it made things harder for me. I was in the middle of trying to work through a rigorous breastfeeding/pumping schedule, and I was sleep deprived and hormonal. I felt stressed about hosting them, feeding them, entertaining them. Even though they said I didn't need to worry about these things, it is in my bones to be the hostess, and I couldn't relax. It was simply one more thing to worry about that I didn't need. And I felt shy about breastfeeding and pumping in front of them – especially my father-in-law – so I'd go up and hide in the nursery every two hours. I couldn't wait for them to leave, as much as I love them.

MG: My father-in-law asked me the day I got home from the hospital how long it would take for me to lose my stomach fat. That didn't go over so well...

MK: Aside from the unsolicited advice that I mentioned earlier, my in-laws insisted on coming to visit for an entire week right when the baby was born. While it was nice to have a hand around the house, it was actually pretty stressful having visitors staying at my house during that time. I wish they had come a couple of weeks later.

SI: - My in-laws came and expected to be taken care of ("what's for lunch?").

- My sister-in-law and brother-in-law came over and brought their two sons (ages four and seven) to meet the baby and stayed for four hours! The boys were so active and one had snot coming down his nose, both my husband and I were a nervous wreck after they left, not to mention their being present made it hard to pump while they were there (I was able to nurse, but not as much as I wanted to, and was so stressed by all the commotion, I am sure it had some effect on me).

- My husband would take pity on me because I was so tired and would feed the baby formula - even after I had said that I was trying to increase my milk supply and to just bring her to me when she was hungry (even if that was only 15 minutes after I had last fed her).

TT1: In-laws would show up to bring food, but would expect us to all sit down and eat dinner at the same time; they just didn't get it. I was pressured into having them visit. They are too high maintenance to help.

Family

AA: They made me so dependent on them that when I started caring for her all by myself I found it very difficult.

EL: Family – too many family dinners that were ill timed.

JD: Having family in the house to help was great, but they were often asking where things were, etc., so it took away from time when I should have been resting.

KP: It would have been really nice to have close family come by and just help out with the household chores that needed to be done, considering so many were coming over to visit. Also, it would be great for spouse to monitor guests. It was so overwhelming to have so many people in and out of the house in such a short period of time. You can barely hold a conversation with one person, much less all of these guests. Limit who comes on any given day. And for those "baby blues" days, have your spouse take charge and "reschedule" visitors for those days. It's too much to have people there when you are an emotional mess and just need time to cry it out. As for friends and family, it is so important not to overstay your welcome. The new family wants to share their joy with you, but they also have a lot to do... like sleep and breastfeed! New moms are not comfortable nursing in front of an audience at first and also are not likely to feel comfortable to excuse themselves to nurse... this will affect supply ultimately forever. So don't overstay your welcome!

Spouse

AC: I wish my husband had complimented me on my pregnant body.

DG: My husband told me when I was annoying him or what I was doing wrong (being too bossy, telling him how to do things). He made suggestions for how I could be more helpful by couching my recommendations in softer language. That just made me mad and bitter, so I wasn't any more helpful to him.

MF: Not enough help in the middle of the night when I was so exhausted I thought I could pass out when I blinked.

MH: My spouse would constantly ask me what to do because I am the mother and, of course, I should know the answers. Every time he asked, I would freeze as I was worried that I wasn't 100% sure what the right answer would be. I felt as though he thought I should know the answers and be right. I was afraid that I would have the wrong answer and that it would cause our son some unknown or unforeseen harm. I wanted my husband to share in some of the burden of being responsible for the wrong decisions/answer.

It is also frustrating when someone gives you advice without a real base of information. If you did not raise a child recently or are not in tune with the recent science or have not read any books/sources of information, do you give your opinion based on your whim!

RA: Husband returned to work on second week. Would have liked him home for two weeks. But I think he was more relaxed because he was able to do a job successfully during the day, so it helped his ego for when he returned to a crying baby whom none of us could console at first. People called the home phone (I didn't know how to turn down the ringer). It woke me/baby from naps, so I wish they'd all use the cell phone which is on vibrate or would text instead...

Mom left after first week…

RO: For a while when it seemed like I was breastfeeding all the time, my husband would ask "are you going to feed her AGAIN?!" in a way that felt very critical. But after we discussed it, he backed off. And a certain unnamed relative loved to take off with my daughter, even if she was crying, and she would just say "oh, babies cry sometimes" without giving her back to me. This drove me crazy because I'm not one to let her cry. Luckily, my baby is past the stage where she will be held against her will.

TT2: My husband complained when the baby had gas and asked me not to eat certain foods. I didn't like being told what I could and couldn't eat. In the end, I had to do what's best for the baby, which for her, meant taking dairy out of my diet.

WC: My husband thought I had postpartum depression when really I was just going through normal hormonal fluctuations. Friends that keep telling me about the one person they know that ran a marathon six months after giving birth to twins.

Anybody and Everybody

AB: Many people that had babies in the 60's and 70's didn't breastfeed – they formula fed because that was the thing to do. They are the first to tell you to just give the kid formula. Do what you want, don't listen to them. My mother-in-law telling me daily that she felt sorry for me for being home with a crying baby – I learned to respond "isn't that what babies do."

AT: Suggesting CIO (crying it out) at the beginning before four months. Suggesting formula to allow me to get some sleep.

BN: Came to visit and then didn't leave.

CB: Well intentioned relatives don't burp the baby the way we found that worked... Old aunties saying, " I know girl...I had my own babies...now you go get your nap..." and I go upstairs worried that the baby won't burp. Sure enough, I come downstairs and the baby is crying, and does three huge burps when we burp her the way that we found works.

DK: Calling constantly, particularly the first week that we were home from the hospital.

JB: Want to see her all the time. Bring the baby to...

JR: They do not live close enough to be helpful.

KF: I really disliked it when people grabbed my baby out of my arms. I know folks want to hold the baby and want to help, but I wanted to figure things out for myself and wanted my new baby in my arms or my husband's. When I invited folks over, I expected they'd want to hold the baby and that was fine, but when people were staying with me for extended periods of time, I didn't want them to hold my baby all the time.

KK2: It would have helped if they stopped telling me to JUST RELAX. It also would have helped if they stopped always wanting to help with baby when what I needed was help with everything else.

KS: Not want to leave the house or stay for too many hours. I would excuse myself to feed the baby, but they didn't want to leave.

LG: They did not realize I needed so much help, and they thought it was best to give us some personal space when, in fact, I needed them to help me, but was too prideful to ask for help myself.

LT: One friend stayed way too long, we should have been napping while my son was, but instead we were speaking with her. Strange because she has two kids, then again, they are older!

MM: Offered advice that seemed ancient or incorrect.

Everyone seems to think they have a better way of taking care of a baby. Don't tell me I'm spoiling my baby because I pick him up when he cries. It gets very annoying and it's downright rude.

OO: Give unwanted advice.

PB: Just come over and sit and stare!

SE: Spouse – assuming that since I was "at home," I could do all the chores and errands that we used to share equally. Family – pressuring me to attend family gatherings and bring the baby when I didn't feel up to it and then getting angry when I declined. Friends – one friend called me everyday to "check in." It got to be a real pain in the butt.

SH: Offer unsolicited advice.

SK1: Sometimes people gave too much advice when I didn't ask for it. :-)

SS: Tell me to "stuff a bottle in that baby's mouth" when the baby is crying.

UG: My friends didn't understand it might take me weeks to return their calls or catch up with them. My family gave unsolicited advice that I didn't think was relevant to my new family or me.

Me

LK: Go back to work too soon, come home late from work.

No Complaints

CV: Nothing. They really were all trying to help me because I was in such pain and having feeding issues.

KK1:   I was lucky – everyone was great.

Kathy's Thoughts:

This is the time in your life when communication is really most important.

Tell people what you need and what you don't need, so the expectations of both you and them are clear. Oh, and somehow, there has to be some scientific research somewhere that correlates new parents' lack of sleep and the fact that your relatives are much more annoying than usual.

Also, keep in mind that everyone loves a baby and usually relishes the opportunity to hold one. Work on making sure your baby is only held when you want him or her to be held by others. I also like the thought of people washing their hands thoroughly before doing so. You can always tell a "baby-hogger" that it's time to breastfeed.

Also, TDaP (Tetanus, Diptheria and acellular Pertussis) vaccine is EXTREMELY important for you and anyone coming in contact with your baby. Pertussis (aka whooping cough) can be fatal for infants. Please ask you healthcare provider for more information.

Suggestions for Encouraging Helpful Things

Question 15. What suggestions do you have for encouraging spouse, family, and/or friends to continue doing the helpful things?

The support of a spouse, extended family, and friends is critical during the early days and weeks postpartum. After the baby is born and the first few days at home pass, people seem to disappear into the woodwork. It would be nice to make plans, so you can avoid this pitfall. Here are some suggestions from our moms.

People Should Know

HM: Don't wait for someone to tell you what they need. If you see unfolded laundry, fold it. You know they need to eat, so bring some damn food. Clean it up afterward. Make their beds. Wash bottles. Bring gifts of magazines and ice cream. Rub feet. Bring the mama a lot of water. Try not to bug her – just do stuff.

JG: Always bring a meal or healthy snack when you go to visit a friend who just had a baby.

Just Ask for What You Want

DS: New parents should ask for help with practical things, like cleaning and cooking before the baby actually comes. It takes all your physical and mental energy to figure out what to do with your baby, and everything else just kind of falls by the wayside, but you can be semi-prepared to take care of that in advance. Other than that... ask if parents need help, but respect them if they say they can't think of anything (unless you're close enough emotionally and geographically to be in their house and see what they need).

HA: Usually people are more than willing to help. Just ask and see.

JD: Remind family, spouse, etc. that every effort really helps because it takes several people to help keep you afloat for the first several days.

KW: Communication is key. People need to know how to help you.

LG: Communicate by asking and telling.

MG: Just ask them directly and let them know how much you appreciate what they are doing.

SI: - Pleading. That seemed to work for me.

- Actually, I would just ask.

TT1: Tell them exactly what you want them to do and thank them.

Talk to them before the birth, so everyone knows what you think you'll want.

WC: Don't be afraid to ask for help. And help may not come from the people you expect.

Be Grateful and Say Thank You

AB: Thank people for the little things they've done.

AT: Validate that you appreciate their help and ask for compromise.

JB: Thank them. Let them know how helpful they are.

JR: Appreciate that they are trying to help and know that they might not always do things the way you would. If you have a list of ways to help and really want certain things accomplished, not only make a list, but prioritize it. Say thank you for all the help you get! Thank you notes are still appreciated.

KC: I made sure to thank them and let them know when something they did or said helped me.

KK1: Just let them know that whatever they are doing is helping and thank them.

KS: Continuously thank them and tell them what a huge help it was to us to bring food over and they would bring more!

LK: Letting them know how much I valued/benefited from their help.

LT: I think as a nursing mom, it's important to remind others that are helping how helpful they are actually being. I always worried that my husband was missing out on stuff with my son because I was nursing, but he never felt that way at all. I think it's important to give positive feedback about what they are or aren't doing.

MF: Positive reinforcement works the best.

PB: Just make sure you say a constant "thank you" and tell them how much you appreciate specific things.

RA: Say THANK YOU.

Tell them how much easier things were because of what they did/said/etc. Be specific with your gratitude.

RO: No matter how beat we both are, I always try to thank my husband for doing things, whether it's washing the dishes or bringing me a glass of water while I pump. It's easy to lose the civility, but for me it's important to not take things for granted.

SE: Tell them how helpful it is and apologize in advance for not getting that "Thank You" note out. You can also send out an e-mail explaining what would be helpful for you and what would not be helpful, addressed to all friends and family, so that no one feels singled out.

SH: Thank them often.

SK2: Express gratitude.

UG: Show your gratitude and thank them profusely for their help. Get them involved with taking care of the baby, such as bottle feeding or giving the baby a bath.

Tips and Suggestions for How to Get Help

AC: Check on mom – ask how I'm doing. Sometimes I'm better at answering questions than volunteering my feelings.

BN: Come, bring food, help clean, and then go home, unless you are the mom of the mom. I wish my mom could have moved in with us! My mother-in-law, not so much.

BW: I think my husband is so sweet because I try to be sweet to him – I'll let him sleep longer in the mornings and take care of the baby, and I'll apologize when I'm grumpy.

CB: Tactful language – "We found that ___works really well." Stay away from phrases like " don't do ___." "Make sure you do ___." Especially to a woman who has had kids and thinks she knows all about babies!

CV: If you are committed to breastfeeding, then you are the only one who can do that (at least until you can pump some extra for bottle feeding, and I think it's recommended to wait three to four weeks to do that if you can). But every other task – meal preparation, laundry, dishes, housecleaning, and errand-running – can be done by someone else. So anything anyone can do to help you have time for yourself to nap, rest, check e-mail, or shower is helpful. Communicating that by expressing your needs and then encouraging and thanking those who help is the best way to get by.

DG: Just don't forget to smile and laugh. Take lots of pictures, even of the screaming and the crying because you'll laugh at them later. We have some great screaming-photos, which are hilarious to look at now.

DK: I've had friends/family offer to babysit which is nice, but it would be more helpful if they would make a specific offer of a time. The few times I've tried to take them up on it, they've been busy, which is understandable, but I would encourage friends/family to say something like "I would love to come over next weekend and help you, so that you can get out of the house. When is a good time for me to do that?"

EL: Divide up tasks to make the list more manageable. Make a wish list and find ways to make your spouse and you both get what you want done.

EM: If family members want to come visit, but are sick or you just aren't comfortable having them touch the baby, keep the baby in a carrier. Hand visitors a receiving blanket to put over themselves before holding the baby if that makes you more comfortable. If they are offended, say that you just fed the baby and the blanket will protect their clothing from spit up. Also, when the baby started to want people's fingers in her mouth, some people enjoy this and really want to put their dirty hands or long sharp fake nails in the baby's mouth. When I could see this coming, I would hand them a teething toy and say that we were trying to train the baby to like the toys. Tell people the things they are doing that are making it easier on you, so they keep doing it.

KG: Put together a calendar of things that need to get done, so you don't have to ask or nag.

KK2: Friends: Continue to offer help long after it would seem necessary.

Spouse: As best as possible, even with lack of sleep, continue to be flexible and give a lot of advance notice if time out needed or other commitment.

Family: Stagger visits to offer most support.

Ask: How can I help you?

KP: Make a list of "chores" that spouse/family/friends could do if they are interested. Hang it somewhere, like on the fridge, so they don't feel obligated, but if they inquire, it's all spelled out, so you don't even have to think about it!

MH: Ask what the new mother or new family needs for help and actually do it. If you are the father, do not constantly ask the mother what should be done. Instead, exert your rights as a father and make some of you own decisions. After all, you are in this together.

MK: If they are local, I would suggest that they come over for an hour or two to help around the house, and then leave, to give you space. If they are out of town, have them wait a couple of weeks to visit. Hire someone to come in and help around the house for a little each day.

MM: A new mother could always use pampers, wipes, baby books, or even a hot meal.

SK1: Taking care of a baby is a full-time job, and anything else you can do to help keep the household running will create a more harmonious environment for everyone!!! Don't let the mother overwork herself or she may lose her smiles and good nature. If mama's happy, everyone is happy.

SS: I heavily encourage this because there are so many emotions that a mother feels and sometimes we need time to ourselves just to sort things out. We do not need all the criticisms of what we are doing wrong, but encouragement is required!

TT2: Some breastfeeding centers have support groups for the support person, which would be helpful and informative. It's important for the mother to ask for what she needs, but sometimes that's hard, so I would suggest asking the mother, "Is there anything I can help with?" at least a couple of times a day.

Kathy's Thoughts:

These are all great thoughts. Communication styles can vary from family to family. The consequences for not communicating your needs right in the beginning, though, can make a big difference in your life. Sounds cliché, of course, but communication is a two-way street. The people around you will not know what you need UNLESS YOU TELL THEM. If they say, "no," you do run the risk of feeling hurt and having your expectations dashed, but at least you know you're on the same page. If you don't ask them at all, you could resent them and not get your needs met.

Getting people's help can preserve your sanity. One of the common ways a person can help is to watch your child so that you can get some rest, take a shower, see the outside world, hang with adults, buy supplies, or do whatever you need to do. You might be fearful of leaving the baby who is constantly breastfeeding and not want to introduce a bottle very soon, so you don't interrupt the breastfeeding relationship. When moms are totally exhausted, I always think it's fine to introduce a bottle of breastmilk earlier than the three- to four-week mark. It may be the thing that preserves breastfeeding. As long as the baby is doing a great job of latching and an orthodontic nipple is only used only once or twice a day, it should not interfere with breastfeeding.

Suggestions for Discouraging Unhelpful Things

Question 16. What suggestions do you have for discouraging spouse, family, and/or friends from doing the things that weren't so helpful?

Although I like to group together similar types of answers, this question generated a range of incredibly varied responses. So in this case, the task of looking for common themes was not helpful. I decided to make an exception here – and everything is going to go under one heading... COMMUNICATE!

Communicate

AB: If it's your mother advising you to formula feed, just ignore her; it's impossible to stop your parents from sharing their advice.

AC: As much as you're committed to a "birth plan," staying focused on the birth/labor process is important. My family came almost immediately after I checked into the hospital for an induction. After two failed attempts, a c-section was performed. That was 48 hours after I arrived! My plan was nothing like I expected it to be. The stress of family filling the waiting room put a great deal of pressure on me. I remember feeling as if I was doing something wrong.

191

AT: Being honest without being critical.

BN: My pediatrician told us to leave a bathrobe by the door. He told us to put it on every time we had guests over. If we wanted the guests to stay a while tell them you just woke up from a nap. If you want them to leave, tell them you were going to take a nap. We didn't try this technique, but I wish we had.

CV: You just have to be clear about your expectations and desires. Before you have the baby, it might make sense to say, "What we THINK we will want is X, Y and Z. But please know that it's hard to know how we'll feel once the baby arrives, so please forgive us if our needs change or we ask something else of you. The most helpful thing you can do for us is be flexible."

DA: Don't ask your spouse "What's wrong" every time she starts having a contraction!

DG: Assume the best in people.

DS: If I could figure out how to get rid of unsolicited, unwanted, unhelpful advice, I'd write my own book and make a zillion dollars.

EL: Just don't do the family dinners – I should have said no to more things, so I could have stayed home and slept.

HA: Being straightforward and just telling them what you didn't like and to please either not do it or do something else.

HM: Don't say, "How can I help?" because that is too open-ended. Ask them, "What is one thing you're worried about? What do you need to do today? What do you WANT to eat?" People, especially new moms, don't want to be a bother and ask for things and help. But there is ALWAYS a way to help. If she says she's tired, offer to stay up with the baby. Insist. You don't have to be a bully – but just make them feel okay with you doing something for them. Never complain afterward. If you stay up with the baby, they don't want to hear how tired you are the next day. Suck it up. It was one night. Offer to do it again next week.

JB: Thank them, but remind them that you can't do all that you used to.

JD: Don't have hyperactive Jewish relatives.

JR: Redirect them to other tasks. Tell them, if you can do it tactfully; otherwise, blame hormones and exhaustion and have your partner do it.

KG: I probably could have used some suggestions in this area.

KS: Tell them that I was really tired and needed to rest or to excuse us that we needed to spend some alone time with the baby.

LG: Communicate with each other.

LT: I think you have to hit it head on and just respectfully say something like "we're not doing things that way."

MF: Open communication is the best gift you can give. Nobody can read your mind.

MG: Tell them directly how unhelpful what they are doing is and set boundaries.

MK: Talk to them about your plans ahead of time (especially breastfeeding). I found that everyone had a different opinion on how frequently I should be breastfeeding, and no one understood that a baby could be hungry every hour for a while. Many people, especially those who formula fed, thought that I was feeding the baby too much and were not shy about expressing their opinions.

MM: Don't judge me for how I am raising my baby. That goes for breastfeeding, bottle-feeding, vaccinations, sleep schedules, etc.

PB: Nicely say that help would be appreciated when they mention coming over.

RA: Thanked them for what was good, and then said it would be most helpful to continue that path, and it was no longer necessary to do/say xyz (that you felt was unhelpful), then remind them of how much you appreciated the efforts that helped.

E.g., Thank you.

RO: Just listen to the mom (even if she's a new mom!) and give her a chance to figure things out in her own way.

SE: Again, an email explaining exactly what you need and what you don't.

SI: I think I would have put my foot down more and talked things out clearly with my husband, so we would be on the same page regarding feedings and guests.

SK1:   Advice is only helpful when it is asked for. The first month is very important for bonding and can really build confidence in the mother. If you continually try to advise, the new mama won't be able to build her own bearings for the rough seas ahead. :-) If you'd like to be used as a resource, show you can respect her new status and her feelings.

SK2:   Explain that I need to do what feels best for me and family, not copy everything that was modeled for me... and stick to it by believing in self and hubbie.

SS: Remember that this is a transition for everyone, and they need to be a bit more sensitive to new mothers.

TT1:   Be honest and clear – it's not the time to be subtle. Preface your honest statements with something to ease them and not make them harsh if your family/friends would be offended.

  If someone just 'doesn't get it,' just don't ask them to help or have them come anymore.

TT2:   I would suggest they ask the mother, "What is working?" "What isn't working?" and "What can I do differently?". And don't take it personally!

UG: Plan in advance and be up front with people about what you need. We told all our friends we weren't accepting visitors for the first month because we needed time to adjust to life with a newborn.

Kathy's Thoughts

What a wide variety of reactions and alternatives! We grow as women and mothers in ways we never thought possible. If I can say one uniquely positive thing about this time in our lives, it's that we usually learn quickly to ask for help, and even when we don't, we still eventually learn how to accept it. Some people do it better than others. Some do it more quickly than others. The sooner you do this, the easier this time of your life tends to be. The bottom line is, we all learn, grow, and change.

As a woman who's closer to being a grandmother than a new mother, I find chapters 15 and 16 helpful for me as well. Perhaps it would be insightful for families and friends to read some of these responses, too!

Helpful Books, Classes, Internet Sites Before Birth

Question 17. Were any books, classes, internet sites, etc. helpful in preparing you for childbirth and breastfeeding?

Some authorities on cognition suggest that there are three basic ways in which we learn. One is called kinesthetic and generally involves learning by doing. Another is visual, involving reading and looking at pictures. The third is called auditory and involves learning by listening. The trick to optimize learning is to identify the individual style that works best for each of us, and that, in turn, requires that we determine which sense is primary.

Keep in mind that the best learning style for one task may be different from the best learning style for other tasks. If you learn best by doing (kinesthetic learning), you are likely to benefit from a childbirth or breastfeeding class where you practice a skill. If you are a visual learner, reference books and illustrated guides may work best. If you are an auditory learner, perhaps you should take advantage of lectures or books on tape. Most of us do not learn in one way to the exclusion of all others. Therefore, you can expect that the best method for learning will be one that incorporates many different senses regardless of our individual style.

Here are our mothers' responses concerning what worked best for them. In some cases, I've separated the answers for categorization.

Books

DG: We relied a lot on *What to Expect*.

HM: I LOVED Anne Lamott's book *Operating Instructions*. It is not about instructions – it is all about being okay with being human and struggling and finding your way.

JD: *The Girlfriend's Guide to Pregnancy* and *Baby 411*.

JR: Most helpful: *Nursing Mother's Companion* by Kathleen Huggins

KG: *The Breastfeeding Book* by Kathleen Huggins was very helpful.

KW: I also loved the book *Girlfriends Guide to Pregnancy*, which cut out the bullshit and included the humor.

MH: I thought *Baby 411* was very helpful in terms of breastfeeding and first getting home with the baby. It gives the necessary information in short bursts, while sprinkling much needed humor.

RA: Your book, Kathy, *Start Here*, for breastfeeding helped.

SH: *The Womanly Art of Breastfeeding*

SS: *The Baby Book* by William and Martha Sears was a very helpful guide to what we could expect and what to do in certain situations. Also, having a good lactation consultant (wink wink) was essential to my child's well being! Going to the baby fair was also pretty helpful. Learned about some useful products.

SW: Loved *The Happiest Baby on the Block* – everything in it makes sense and is very readable. Helped me calm my baby and make decisions to soothe and calm her appropriately.

TT2:   I found that reading books while I was going through the issues was helpful. I'm not sure I would have absorbed as much prior to having the baby because I just couldn't relate until it was really happening.

UG: The book *Be Prepared* is extremely funny and provides good, practical advice for new parents.

Classes

AA: I attended childbirth classes, and the breathing exercises they taught me were extremely helpful during labor.

AB: I took a Hypno-Birthing class. The Hypno-Birthing class was wonderful in providing techniques to cope with natural childbirth.

BW: The Lamaze Class at my local hospital and the book *Breastfeeding Basics*. I went to a local lactation business for a free class that was helpful, too.

CV: We took an infant care and breastfeeding class from our hospital where we delivered, and both were helpful.

DK: I had a great childbirth teacher (also helpful with some breastfeeding prep).

Not a big fan of books except to answer specific questions/address problems.

MK: We attended a childbirth preparation class before the baby was born. In hindsight, I definitely wish we had done a bit more!

RB: I took a one-on-one childbirth class that helped me deal with labor. I also took a breastfeeding class, which was helpful as well. In both cases, I felt more informed going into it.

SK2: Yes. Class at OB/GYN office for basics and Ida May book on childbirth. Also read *The Birth Book: Everything You Need to Know to Have a Safe and Satisfying Birth* (Sears Parenting Library).

TT1: For childbirth – Bradley Natural Childbirth Class – really, any education to let you know what your options are, so that whatever you choose, you can be confident and know that you made the best decision given the circumstances.

The two-day Lamaze class at the hospital is just not enough time to be prepared. It gave us great specific information on how things worked at our hospital. A multi-week class that makes you think about it every day for two months or more prepares you.

UG: The local hospital offers child prep and breastfeeding classes, both were helpful.

DVDs

KK1: *The Happiest Baby on the Block* DVD was very helpful. I also found I got a lot out of watching baby care and breastfeeding videos on You Tube. I did not find my childbirth class helpful at all.

Many Things

AC: I read books and magazines, took classes from the local hospital, and had a weekly update from a baby website, but I really prided myself in "knowing a little about a lot." I never went to an appointment expecting to know as much as the doctor or have him affirm or refute what I had read. It was important to me to have my chosen health care provider guide me – not the media.

AT: Kellymom.com, yoga nidra, prenatal yoga, book *Parenting From the Inside Out.*

BN: *Happiest Baby on the Block* was fabulous! *The Girlfriend's Guide to Pregnancy and the First Year* made me happy. I hated my birthing class, but I made one of my closest friends in my class. We had girls eight days apart and hung out during our maternity leaves.

EL: Yoga and Hypno-birthing book (Marie Mongan) and CDs - kept me calm during my pregnancy and helped with my breathing during labor and delivery

Happiest Baby on the Block; babycenter.com weekly updates.

HA: The Dr. Karp video was great, though we saw it well after giving birth. And your book, *Start Here: Breastfeeding and Infant Care* was good, full of practical info and not huge. Some of the other books out there try to put so much info in there that it's really overkill and sometimes is actually wrong. Especially for me, English is not my native language, so a shorter book was welcome.

JB: Babycenter.com, Lamaze class, Fit pregnancy magazine and web page.

KC: I loved the weekly email updates from babycenter.com and whattoexpect.com. The information on the site was helpful to browse as well, but their weekly updates explaining how my baby was changing and what I might be feeling were usually spot on, and I looked forward to learning why I was feeling what I was feeling. I took a CPR class at the hospital, which put my mind at ease a bit.

KF: I liked *Baby 411* and What to Expect's website (www.whattoexpect. com). Nothing could have really prepared me for breastfeeding. I took a childbirth and breastfeeding class, but more than anything it made me feel like I did my due diligence, like I was prepared. Nothing can really prepare you though.

KK2: I absolutely loved and read cover-to-cover: *The Girlfriends' Guide to Surviving the First Year of Motherhood* (written in the late 90's, so a bit dated, but never have laughed so hard!) by Vicki Lovine and my Bradley/Brio birth instruction/instructor doula!

KS: Took classes, which were helpful, through a local maternity store and my local hospital. Loved the babycenter.com site with weekly advice on where you were and where the baby was at every stage.

RO: I love, love, loved my prenatal yoga. It was very helpful in preparing for all aspects of childbirth, parenting, and breastfeeding, both physically and mentally. It was also great to spend some time every week with other moms in the same situation. On the other side of things, I grew to despise all books related to pregnancy. I was reading to Tom one night that the book listed "irrational fears" as a symptom of pregnancy. I will never forget that he replied that irrational fears weren't caused by pregnancy, but by reading the pregnancy books! So true.

Websites

EM: Mostly just the www.Kellymom.com website.

JG: The March of Dimes website was helpful in letting me know I was in pre-term labor and needed to go to the emergency room right away.

KG: Twitter parties about breastfeeding are great for questions and answers/advice as well. Leaky Boob's page on FaceBook.

KW: Babycenter.com is a good resource for day-to-day questions about pregnancy and childbirth.

LK: Listserves, like the birth club with my expected due date month on ivillage...

kellymom.com about breastfeeding.

Dr. Hale's website for BF/drug interactions.

LT: Kellymom website. *Ina May's Guide to Breastfeeding* book, classes at my local hospital, Kathy McCue!

MF: Babycenter.com is the best website EVER!

MH: www.kellymom.com was very helpful with giving information on breastfeeding and how to deal with issues surrounding breastfeeding.

RA: Kelly mom site.

SK1: Loved kellymom.com, but I also used that to self diagnose a little too much.

WC: Baby center website was really good.

Nothing ☹

DS: Honestly, everything I'd read, planned, or hoped for went out the window when my water broke 5½ weeks early, and I've heard from a lot of other women that their birth plans quickly followed suit once they were actually in labor. I think a brief overview of the physical process of childbirth and the prevalent options during labor (medication, support, etc.) would have been more helpful than the half-dozen books I read that gave me more information than I could remember, along with unrealistic expectations of what I could dictate during labor and delivery. I wish I'd had a breastfeeding book, but I didn't see any until after I had my baby.

KP: Unfortunately, I think the best way to be informed about childbirth and breastfeeding is just to experience it. The two courses I took through the hospital were informative, but not really helpful "in the moment." Both are best learned by doing...

LG: Somewhat to a certain degree, nothing can fully prepare you for the first time.

PB: Not really, to be honest.

SI: I must admit I didn't do much of any pre-birth prep, which I regret. I would get so overwhelmed by the amount of information out there that I would get anxious. It felt like a test with a final (actually it felt like the Bar exam only worse). I did look at babycenter.com and found it helpful. I tried to relax as much as possible and enjoy the pregnancy – which I did. It was one of the happiest times in my life, only to be surpassed by what my time with the baby is like now.

Friends and Professionals

CV: If you have friends who have babies a few months before you, it's also helpful to hang around them late in pregnancy and watch them do everything – diapering, bathing, and especially nursing.

MG: Mostly talking to you, Kathy!

SE: My best resource was my friend's mother who was a pediatric nurse. She spent a lot of time with me and really helped me to feel calm. I found Lamaze class useful for its information, but useless in practice. If you are going to do natural childbirth, you need to evaluate yourself honestly.

Kathy's Thoughts

These responses each offer useful information. The variety of options outlined above makes it likely that there will be some suggestions that will appeal to you and will best fit your special learning style. The emergence of a highly accessible body of knowledge through the internet offers new avenues for you to seek out information that were not available even a few years ago. Moms may want to go online and look at some of these resources. Pay attention to the sources and seek out reputable organizations and authors. Look for evidence-based research. You will have to assess the reliability of this information yourself. Books and websites should speak to both your heart and your head.

Before this questionnaire, I had never heard of Hypno-Birthing, but now that I mention it to moms, I've discovered how well it works for some women.

Helpful Books, Classes, Internet Sites After Birth

Question 18. Were any books, classes, internet sites, etc. helpful AFTER the baby arrived?

Most of the resources cited in the previous chapter helped moms prepare for childbirth and the start of breastfeeding. After giving birth, the resources that moms need necessarily change. Every succeeding month in your young baby's life brings new situations and new challenges, so the tools you rely on have to change, too.

Parents spend tremendous amounts of energy on preparing for the birth of their child. There is no question this is necessary. But once your baby arrives, then what? The actual amount of time spent in nurturing a baby and raising a child dwarfs the time devoted to childbirth itself. The weeks and months after the birth event itself are critical and require your attention and preparation, too.

I'm reminded of the story of the couple that spent so much time preparing for their wedding that all they wanted to do on their honeymoon was sleep. If you've had a child already, this should remind you of the first week or two after giving birth. If you haven't, you will remember this analogy when the time comes, hopefully with a smile. There is no substitute for preparation.

The responses that follow are not categorized. The individual thoughts are unique to each respondent.

AA: *Positive Discipline* is one book that I found helpful.

AB: *The Baby Whisperer* describes a philosophy on understanding the needs of your newborn infant. I've found internet sites, such as Kellymom and exclusivelypumping.com, very helpful.

AC: There's an answer for everything on the net – just type away. I like to ask a real person first.

AT: Kellymom.com, moms' group

BW: Ahhh… It's a Baby, Now What? at my local hospital – it could've been a good class, but the instructor was not very good.

CB: NONE. Nothing happened the way the birth classes said. I was induced and had a c-section. They need to have a c-section class! Even the breastfeeding class before birth was NOT helpful…that's a learn by doing kind of thing, and I benefited from individual instruction.

DC: Urban Mom (A Washington, DC, area listserve)

DS: *What to Expect: The First Year* answered lots of my questions about normal baby development. I think that's really the only one I used.

EL: *What to Expect During the First Year;*

Happiest Baby on the Block;

Baby Sign Language Basics - Marta Briant;

Healthy Sleep Habits, Happy Child

HA: The Stanford breastfeeding video was good.

HM: Kellymom.com was a huge help and source of information. YOU, Kathy McCue, were a tremendous help. You were just available to answer questions and encourage me, and gave me permission to stop when I was going crazy. I would never have made it as long as I did without you. I wish I'd had your first book then!

JB: *You're A Mom Now What* (a book), babycenter.com, Parenting Magazine, Kellysmom.com

JD: *Baby 411*, AAP's book on caring for your baby

JG: I found a local infant group and a new moms' group. Both of which were very helpful.

JR: General overview of the birthing process, hospital tours, breastfeeding class, and a yoga class in which the moms shared experiences about their births and/or birth plans.

Other books: *Super Baby Food Book*, *Baby Bargains* (for the stuff you need), *Baby 411*, and *Girlfriend's Guide to Pregnancy.*

KC: *The Happiest Baby on the Block* (the book and especially the video). This ended up being extremely helpful for us. Swaddling was like religion in our family; *The No Cry Sleep Solution*; www.adviceforbaby.com

KF: Honestly, I felt like information was my enemy. It just made me SO insecure. I think that it makes sense to have information, but I'd urge folks not to get too caught up in it. It's easy to allow information to freak you out. I did.

KK1: I've enjoyed my Dr. Sears' *The Baby Book* and the websites www.wholesomebabyfoods.com and www.kellymom.com.

KK2: Babycenter.com (before and after), as well as: *The Baby Book* and *The Portable Pediatrician* by Dr. William Sears.

KS: Babycenter.com was what I found to help the most with different stages weekly.

KW: *Baby 411 - A Guide to Childcare in the First Year*. Again - wish I'd read it before the baby arrived.

I like kellymom.com for breastfeeding questions.

LG: *What To Expect When You're Expecting* and *What To Expect The First Year*.

LT: Kelly mom, Ina May's book on childbirth, and Kathy!

MF: Babycenter.com is the best website EVER!

MG: I got a ton of books. I read chapters of many of them. Then I went back to work, got totally overwhelmed, and stopped reading. Now I just ask my neighbor who has a baby who is the same age as my girls what she is reading (she has not gone back to work yet), and then I copy her!

MH: I thought *Baby 411* was helpful. I also like the American Academy of Pediatrics book *Caring for Your Baby and Young Child*.

MM: Babycenter.com is the best website thus far. I only wish there were local 'mom' groups I could go to once a month or so.

OO: Baby Wise

PB: I read several Sears books, the La Leche book on breastfeeding, and *Making More Milk* by Diane West. I regularly go to Dr. Newman's website and the www.kellymom.com website.

RA: *Happiest Baby on the Block* DVD

Healthy Sleep Habits – Happy Baby (I know you said it isn't good, but what I read prior to your saying that is how to read the baby's tired/drowsy signs. From that day forward, we have ALWAYS gotten her up to bed without the meltdowns we had previously. EVERY night she's telling us in her way to take her up and she just goes to sleep... it is wonderful. I'm not so lucky with naps, but it isn't bad, and we've had much less crying. I also learned from it that babies her age need two to three naps per day: 9:00 am, noon, afternoon naps.)

RB: One book that was helpful early on and has been helpful since then was the American Academy of Pediatrics *Heading Home With a Newborn*. Short easy-to-read chapters that were packed with info, usually reduced my stress level, and often made me laugh with its sense of humor.

Harvey Karp's video was great, too. Your book was helpful, too. I remember thinking that even the introduction (whatever that very first page was) was helpful to me. There are many people who will give you advice and my job is to figure out what makes sense for me. Sure maybe there are "better" ways to do something, but that's OK... not everything is going to be perfect.

RO: I like Kelly Mom and the LactMed site for breastfeeding information. I also have *The Nursing Mother's Companion*, which has good information, but I find it a little disorganized. I don't have much use for the books about babies because you can drive yourself crazy trying to identify "normal." For both pregnancy and parenting, I think the best information comes from health care providers who know you and your child. I'm a scientist, so I tend to look things up in the primary scientific literature, and then integrate what I learn there with information from health care providers. It helps me ask the right questions and be sure that I'm not missing anything.

SE: I generally try and stay off the web because I find it too overwhelming and too loaded with rumors and myths, and a lot of stuff you really don't need to worry about. If I have specific questions, I prefer to ask the pediatrician or a trusted friend.

SH: *Baby 411*

SI: American Academy of Pediatricians book;

Kellymom.com;

Babycenter.com

SK1: I've been reading the *Healthy Sleep Habits, Happy Child* book to learn how to help her with sleeping. So far I really like his ideas....

SK2: Yes. Websites showing correct latches/suck patterns, manually expressing milk, books called... *Baby 411*, *What to Expect the First Year*, *Getting Organized for your New Baby (Before and After)*, *Nursing The First Two Months*.

SS: *The Baby Book* was the most helpful, as well as Mrs. McCue.

TT1: Babycenter.com; local hospital's moms' group facilitated by two nurses.

TT2: The American Academy of Pediatrics' *Caring for your Baby and Young Child*

UG: DC Urban Mom (a local list-serve in the Washington, DC area), kellymom.com, *Healthy Sleep Habits, Healthy Child*

WC: I joined PACE. Such a great support system.

Kathy's Thoughts

In many ways, you have control over the weeks after childbirth. You can make it exciting and look on each incremental step as a gift. And you can also look for ways to avoid the letdown that some moms feel. There is nothing that can happen to you that has not already happened to thousands of other new moms, so there are many proven paths that have been taken to respond. Seek wisdom in available resources and options for learning. There are some really excellent resources mentioned above that clinical evidence fully supports. The American Academy's book *Heading Home with Your Newborn* is a great resource, for example.

You may find that other resources don't fit your personal situation. For obvious reasons, I am not a big fan of material that appears to discourage breastfeeding. I lean heavily toward attachment parenting. I recommend the material of Dr. William Sears. Having parents actively seek to be sensitive and emotionally available for their infant resonates with me.

Words in books are often taken literally, as gospel. You are the best judge of what works or doesn't work. In your family, it only works when it works for you and your baby. So look at resources as collections of thoughts from individuals with experience that moms and dads can try on for size. Also, because of the rapid changes that occur with a newborn, parents need to consider the level of development of their baby when assessing the merits of some of these methods. Enough said.

On the subject of schedules, I try to have moms organize their baby's day so there is always a definite daytime and a definite nighttime. We are tuned to the cycle of days and nights. It's helpful to stop swaddling during the day because swaddling blunts feeding cues. When a baby is swaddled only at bedtime, the swaddling itself will help to promote better sleeping at night. A cool bedroom (between 69 and 71 degrees) and a white noise machine (sounding like a radio stuck between stations) are always on my list of things that can facilitate sleep.

Other Comments/Suggestions

Question 19. Anything not covered by the above questions that you'd like to convey?

Although my questionnaire was supposed to glean all the information you might need, I just knew there would be great information outside the lines. It's always worth it to ask an open-ended question like this. Some people will fill out the rest of the questionnaire, so they can have the chance to answer this question. Here's all of that extra advice from moms, with a little from me, too.

AC: I think I had/have a case of postpartum depression... I find it difficult to admit when I need help.

BN: You were so helpful, Kathy! I also liked the *Girlfriend's Guide to the First Year*; it helped me know that being weepy was normal and I did not have postpartum depression.

BW: It'd be helpful to know what you should have to start breastfeeding:

- Nipple cream

- A few breastfeeding tops

- Pads

- Pillow

- Vitamin D Supplement

Also, tips on building milk surplus and tips on storing and keeping milk.

CV: For some new parents, they are just so in love, and the exhaustion and life changes pale in comparison to how amazing the experience is. For others, though, like me, it can be so difficult in the moment to think you will ever get through this new experience. Everything changes in your marriage and your life, and there's not a whole lot you can do to prepare for that. It is exhausting beyond explanation, so much so that I wondered why no one warned me, but I then realized no one really could. You just have to live it to understand it. But you DO come out the other end of it. There is a light at the end of the tunnel. You get more and better sleep. You get used to getting woken up, and then you get used to not sleeping enough. And these helpless criers turn into children with personalities who amaze you. It is the most rewarding experience life can give you. You discover a new appreciation for your own parents and what they did for you before your first memories. You learn what selflessness and love really are. And there is no life without children that could ever compare to life as the journey through parenthood.

DA: Best piece of advice I've gotten about pumping at work, I'd like to share: Have as many sets of parts as you plan to pump during the day, if you can, so you don't have to worry about cleaning parts during the day (since that adds a lot of time!). Clean everything at night, so you can just pump and put away.

My description/experience with D-MER:

My daughter will be four months old this week. I have had to be almost exclusively a pumper. My daughter did not gain weight in her first month, so the doctors wanted to know precisely how much breastmilk she was taking in. And now that I'm back to work, I'm having to pump anyways, but do nurse her once daily.

I'm a trained social worker, so I have a little bit more than the average familiarity with mental health and I've had a few bouts of major depression throughout my life.

I have not had any postpartum depression (knock on wood). Thinking I was a strong candidate for it, I've been on prozac since she was born. Who knows if I would have gotten PPD without it, but better not to have found out.

I started saying to my therapist when my daughter was about three months old that the only time I feel "weepy" (that's the word I use most, but I really like homesickness, which I see some others use to describe it) is when I'm about to have a let-down. I have a very strong physical sensation during let-downs. My reactions, both psychologically and physically, are strongest when the let-down is spontaneous (i.e., not while nursing or pumping). It has gotten to the point when I can, with 100% accuracy, say I'm about to let down within 30 seconds-one minute. The weepiness/the uneasiness in the pit of my stomach goes away as soon as I let down. It still happens when I'm nursing or pumping, but it doesn't hit me as hard. I think maybe because I'm expecting it, which I'm not when it happens spontaneously. I kept telling my therapist there HAD to be something with the hormones that tell my body it's time to let down that was causing this.

I describe these feelings as a nuisance – it's annoying. I've never thought about giving up breastfeeding because of it; I just wish it would stop. My husband says he can see it on my face now – he can say "You're about to have a let down, aren't you?" On the other hand, I know as soon as I let down, the feelings will go away, so I literally started telling myself "Wait for it…" and then a relieved "There it is…" and I move on.

DK: I think my current thoughts are about being home on maternity leave, and then returning to work. It would be nice to have something written about that.

The first half of my maternity leave I felt like every day was Wednesday. You never have that Monday dread – but you never get to Friday. Time also took on a whole different meaning when you are living in three hour increments of feedings. A day is literally 24 hours, and at the end of a week, I often felt like a month had gone by. These were not bad/negative feelings, but they were different and hard for someone not going through it to understand.

Going back to work – you go from one extreme to another. Spending 24 hours a day with this little creature to only seeing them for a couple of hours. That is difficult – particularly the first week or two, but for me (and for most), it does get better and you get into a rhythm.

DS: I sent this facebook message to a friend a few weeks ago, and she sent me a reply tonight, which made me go back and read the original message. It seemed somehow appropriate to include, even though some of it I've already covered... it seems to be the thing I tell new parents the most.

"How is motherhood treating you? Don't worry, the day is coming where you will sleep five or six straight hours, and you will be convinced that you are the world's worst mother because you let your child die... then you will realize that the baby is crying and your boobs feel like rocks from all the extra milk they've accumulated. And it will all be OK. And then the next night, you'll go to bed expecting a nice long chunk of sleep, only to discover that baby has no intention of repeating that blissful experience again for weeks! But someday, you and she will sleep all the way through the night, and it will be amazing. In the meantime, I kept chanting "This too shall pass" and "The days are long, but the years are short," which are both SO true."

EL: Using cloth diapers seems to cure a diaper rash overnight. They are much easier to use than I thought, especially when I can use 2theroot diaper service. Love them. And Bummis diaper covers are the best – so cute and catch most leaks. Use them with diaper snappies.

Favorite baby items – Baby Bjorn bouncer (what the baby does when I pump), the Lamaze playmat that moves, the Fisher-Price lamb swing, and Bright Starts vibrating chair. I use all of them all over the house – they give me 15-30 minutes, and the baby loves them.

EM: For me, breastfeeding is a whole style of parenting – mostly because in the beginning it's one of the most sure-fire ways to comfort the baby. When our baby first came, it really alarmed my family how often I nursed the baby. They kind of made fun of me and found it very insulting and inconvenient that I would constantly "take her away" to nurse. Because they are formula feeding parents, they had to be more inventive in comforting babies when it wasn't mealtime. So they really thought that it was stupid that I would constantly stick the baby on the breast when she was upset. "Babies just cry," they would tell me. They wanted to try all kinds of other things to comfort the baby, just so I wouldn't take her away to nurse her. My point is that for some families, breastfeeding is just such a new thing that it creates misunderstandings. For some reason, it makes some people really uncomfortable. I am so glad that I didn't do what my family told me to do and "put my baby on a schedule" or avoid nursing when she wasn't "supposed" to be hungry – because she ended up having a tongue-tie and really needed all that nursing time due to inefficient nursing.

JG: If you have a challenging pregnancy or birthing experience, be open to seeking help from someone. There are a lot of resources out there to help moms with the healing process. If you are not into talking with a counselor, there are alternatives, such as art therapy, cranial sacral therapy, and many more, so you can find something in your comfort zone.

JR: - Learn about local consignment/resale shops – these can be a good source for clothes and some other baby stuff.

- Any information on nursing while pregnant... this does not seem to be well covered.

- Let parents know it is ok if their kids do not use a pacifier – embrace the fact that your kid does not want one.

- Travel early and often. Two months to about eight months is the best time to fly with small children. They sleep through most of the flights. After that, they get squirmy. Still take them.

- Try to leave the house once a day. It is good for everyone and stimulates the baby and builds the immune system.

- All advice is an opinion to be followed, interpreted, or ignored as you see fit. You are the mom.

- If you are interested in a Doula, find out about training programs in your area. All Doulas in training are required to attend births for their certification, so they are free.

- Decide about breastfeeding before you go to the hospital. It is best if hospital staff know that you are breastfeeding, and it should help keep them from offering your child a pacifier or bottle, which can be confusing to the baby.

- Always have your partner escort the baby in the hospital for tests, weigh-ins, etc. Someone should know what is actually happening to your baby. At 1-36 hours, your child cannot fight for themselves, if needed.

- Plan to wear maternity clothes for four months after giving birth, if you are out of them before that... great for you.

- It takes nine months up and at least nine months down. Your body will be different, even if your weight is the same as pre-birth.

** Born five hours post due date, so a full-term healthy baby.

KK2:   Get a doula! Be flexible and remember, "It's okay to be mediocre."

KW: Yes, I'd like to remind everyone that nothing is permanent. I've learned that every complication I've had with breastfeeding and/ or care of my baby is fleeting and will get better. I tend to worry and fret, and try to figure out and fix every little thing that comes along in an effort to control the situation. But I'm getting better at realizing that unexpected things happen and will happen. This baby is a living, growing human being who has bad days and good days just like I do... Roll with it, Momma!

On a visit to the pediatrician's office, I received the best little one-liner I could have asked for from my doctor. I was expressing to her my concern about some little thing that I was greatly worried about... I can't even remember now what it was if that tells you anything... She calmly looked me in the eye, put her hand on my shoulder, and said, "This too shall pass."

MH: There is not much information out there regarding the typical growth spurts.

I was not prepared for the six-week growth spurt when my baby starting eating every hour and each feeding lasted around 1½ hours.

Also, I was not prepared for the 12-week growth spurt to last TWO WEEKS! I hear that two weeks is unusual, but I think mothers need to know the growth spurt could be anywhere from one day to two weeks.

I would add somewhere in your book that one should keep a copy of their receipt/proof of purchase for their breastpumps. I had an issue with my Freestyle. Medela would have liked for me to provide them with a copy of my receipt. I no longer had it and they still replaced my unit, but had I known, I would have kept the receipt.

MK: I guess I would just add that, while I have faced my share of hurdles with breastfeeding, it has been such a wonderful experience, and I would do it all over again if given the chance!

MM: Ice chips are a pregnant and nursing mother's best friend. If you're lucky, invest in a fridge/freezer with an automatic icemaker – or if you know you plan on having kids, go ahead and buy that fridge/freezer that makes crushed ice. The hubbies don't like to refill the trays for some reason.

RO: For moms who pump, I recommend investing in multiple sets of pump parts. I pump three times/day, so I have three sets. I bring all the clean parts in one large ziploc bag, and after I use them, I wipe them out with the Medela quick clean wipes, and then move them to a separate bag for used parts. That way, I can wash them at home instead of in the lunchroom. It saves time and the awkwardness of explaining what a breast shield is to inquisitive co-workers.

SK1:   Remember to trust your instincts and don't get too worked up. Time will heal and make things easier...

SS: I wish that I had paid more attention to the nutritional aspect when being pregnant. I over ate and did not really eat healthy. This did not assist my body in any way. Although I am back down to my original pre-pregnancy weight, it was very hard losing all of it. It would have been easier if I ate properly and exercised more.

TT1:   For childbirth, LEARN about all your options and the consequences. Talk about and make decisions before you go into labor so, when faced with decisions, you are sure you know about the procedures and options and can feel confident in the moment that you are doing the best you can.

Kathy's Thoughts

There are some great comments here. I think the question about the mom wanting some "back-to-work" thoughts was a very valid one. Whether to return to work is a big decision for some moms, and even when the decision is made, the process of doing it can be very difficult. Even moms who really have no choice still have to confront many issues. For example, finding childcare can be a monumental task because, seriously... who (other than your own mother) is going to be able to take care of your baby the way you do. I'm here to tell you that although nobody can ever replace you, there are very loving, experienced women who can and do substitute for you when you're away.

There are moms in my practice who can afford nannies, and who bring them for visits to make sure we're all on the same page with regard to growth and development. There are bonds that are created between mothers and caretakers that are very close and remain for years after the child grows. The key bond is one of shared child rearing. The good of the child is their only goal.

Look for one of these women if you're trying to find an in-home nanny, or even if you nanny share (where you and one or two other families hire a mutual nanny who may alternate homes or just use one of the homes). Since there are no rules, you can pretty much arrange whatever is palatable to everyone.

You don't have to be particularly well off to have a great relationship with a caretaker or caretaker organization. The keys are competence, trust, and continuity. Group daycare centers can be very reliable because there's never the fear of your nanny being sick or on vacation. It can also be nice for children to be in the company of other children as they develop and need to socialize. As with any child-related decision, make sure you feel comfortable with the choice.

With all the pros and cons, one thing that has to remain stable for moms who go back to work and continue to breastfeed is the pumping schedule. You should find a place that is appropriate for the task and establish a routine. Then you should stick to it. I usually advise moms to pump once prior to leaving the house in the AM (after breastfeeding), then in roughly evenly spaced periods at mid morning, lunchtime, and in the midafternoon.

I know of a few moms who are in situations where they feel they can pump while they drive to work. I'm not sure of the impact of this activity on safe driving, so I can't really recommend it. (I don't want to read about a serious pumping-related accident in the paper, or even read about the first distracted by pumping driving ticket.) These moms have presumably limited their risk by driving on low-traffic country roads, wearing a hands-free pumping bra, and using a pump that, once plugged into the cigarette lighter with an adapter, they can promptly ignore. They also know that the primary objective is still to get to work safely. I doubt even they would take the risk of pumping on a crowded expressway or where other drivers are unpredictable. By the time they get to work, they have two full bottles and feel like they're getting a jump on the day. Personally, I'd prefer they get to work fifteen minutes earlier, but it does suggest that there are many ways to deal with the return to work.

What I Wish I knew About Early Motherhood – An Essay by KF

This mom preferred to write an essay instead of answering a questionnaire. Here are her musings.

What I Wish I Knew About Early Motherhood

An Essay by KF

On Saturday, my son and I went to the farmers market. We picked up our csa (my baby loves supporting local agriculture!) (Kathy's note - CSA is community supported agriculture), and one of the staff there engaged us in conversation. She, too, is a mom and her babe is about 1½ years old now. She asked me how things were going, and then quickly said, "It gets better. It gets much better." I worry about what my face conveyed to her, because my words were all positive. Still, early motherhood is challenging. I haven't been a mom for very long – only six weeks – but there are already some things that I really wish I had known ahead of time. I don't know if knowing these things would've changed my experience, but I still wish that I had known.

1. Overachievers Beware: Motherhood Cannot Be Aced.

I like to do things well, really well, and better than other people. I take great pride in my work and took great pride in my school work. I went to graduate school full time, while working full time and made sure that my grades were stellar. After I took up running, I decided that I needed to run a marathon. When I do something, I want to do it as well as I possibly can. This attitude is great in the workplace and at school, but it is not helping me so much now. In fact, I think it's making things tougher. I find myself questioning things every day because I want to do everything perfectly. But it's hard to be a perfect consoler or breastfeeder or swaddler. And while doctors and friends can offer suggestions, the reality is that my baby and I need to figure out what he needs and what makes him feel safe and happy. And more frustrating still – those needs and wants are going to change and change and change. Perfection just doesn't live here, so I'm trying to let go of some of my overachiever attitude. I think it's healthy to want to be a good mom, but striving to be a perfect mom is making me insecure. I just don't think motherhood can be aced.

2. Breastfeeding Can Be Really Hard.

I know that I'm not supposed to say that, and I'm sure that it isn't true for everyone, but it's too true for me not to mention it. My baby and I have been very lucky to have a lot of resources to help us out – nursing staff at the hospital, lactation consultant at baby's doctor's office, breastfeeding class instructor, and two moms in my life that breastfed their babies – and I've still found it really challenging. Every time I think I've resolved our last problem, another issue arises. Most recently, I've been troubleshooting having too much milk. This is annoying because just a couple of weeks ago, I was working to increase my milk supply for my ravenous little babe.

I guess I thought that I'd learn how to do it and that would be the end of it. The reality is that it's been a learning process – problems arise and we've had to work through them. Hopefully, we're nearing the end of the learning process, but who knows? Soon, I'll have to go back to work, and we'll need to figure out how to work more regular pumping into my schedule.

The problems are not insurmountable, but it's harder and more time consuming than I expected.

3. Information Can Be Helpful. Or Not.

I read a few books in advance of my baby's arrival. I took a childcare class and a breastfeeding class. I talked to other moms and dads. Often, this information has helped me and first baby, as we've worked to figure out the parenting thing. Sometimes though, I wish I didn't have the internet or *Baby 411* at my fingertips. First, it's made me jump to conclusions. For example, I've had some issues with my breasts. When I googled the symptoms and referred to the books, it seemed likely that I had thrush. So I headed to the doctor, where I was assured that I was perfectly healthy. That's when I was told that breastfeeding can be painful for some people. Which brings me to the second reason that I don't always love having so much info: In general, the books and the classes talk about average experiences. For example, all of the books say that breastfeeding might hurt during the first couple of weeks, but then it does not hurt. They go on to say that if you do experience pain, then you're doing something wrong or there is something wrong with you. But that's just not always true, and I wish the books would say that.

And sometimes they leave info out altogether. For example, everyone talked about how quickly I would get my figure back if I breastfed. Frankly, that's not why I was breastfeeding, but it seemed like a nice benefit. What the books and people left out is that you actually feel your uterus contracting back into its original size. It's not painful, but it's really bizarre. Every time I fed my son, I felt my uterus contracting back into shape. The process is pretty incredible; I could see my belly shrink every day. I just didn't expect that I would feel it all happen.

I'm sure that there are more learnings to come. :)

What I Wish I Knew About Early Motherhood – An Essay by AD

Another mom chooses to write an essay to tell her story, which she feels will help others.

AD – An Essay

A couple of weeks before my daughter was born, I attended a breastfeeding workshop offered at the hospital where I was scheduled to deliver her. My husband had faithfully attended all six weeks of the birthing classes with me, but spending an entire Saturday talking about breastfeeding was above and beyond the call of duty in his eyes. I didn't push, but was disappointed when I realized that there was only one other woman there without her husband, and this woman was not actually married – her boyfriend had to work that day. A conscientious student, I paid close attention to the instructor and even took some notes, but it was hard to really fathom what it would be like to feed my baby in this way. I figured that it would make a lot more sense once I had my baby in my arms, and focused my worries on how I was going to get through the pain of a natural delivery. I practiced my breathing at home, read as much as I could, and made my husband read as much as I could force him too as well.

Ten days before I was due, I woke up in the morning before work feeling unusual. Unable to get back to sleep, I went into the bathroom and sat on the toilet, assuming that I needed to go to the bathroom, and that once I did, I'd feel better and could get another hour of sleep before the alarm. However, as I pushed a bit to move my bowels, I felt a pop and water trickling down my leg – my water had broken! Having second thoughts, I decided to try a little experiment and hopped in the shower, dried off, and checked to see if the water was still coming down my legs. Then, I knew it was real. When I went to the hospital, they sent me back home because the contractions were still far apart. "Go grab some lunch and enjoy these last few hours of freedom!" the nurse had told me. But no sooner had I gotten home than I was doubled over in pain and on my way back to the hospital a second time. The pain was unbearable by the time I got to a room, and the nurse, who also happened to be the mother of a friend of mine from high school, told me, "Don't worry, honey. We're going to give you something for the pain." All plans for a natural, drug-free delivery were out the door. I trusted this woman completely and willingly accepted whatever she could do to make the sharp pains shooting through my back go away.

The back labor turned out to be a problem, as the baby was trying to turn around and could not. Its heartbeat kept going down, as did mine. After about five hours, the nurses ushered my mom, my dad, and my sister out of the delivery room, instructed my husband to change into scrubs, and wheeled me down the hall for a c-section. I spent the next hour or so crying, first from fear, then from emotion and drugs, and finally from the joy of holding my child, a daughter.

Because of the c-section, I had the advantage of four days in the hospital, where the nurses would help me get my screaming child to latch on to my breast and would wheel her away at night, so I could get some sleep. Every time I needed to feed her, I could push the call button and eventually someone would come to guide Colette to my breast. Breastfeeding was tied with lack of sleep for the most difficult aspects of that first week. The pain in my abdomen was severe, but I knew it would get better with time. What I couldn't envision was how I was going to be able to feed my daughter without the help of the nurses, and how I was going to be able to sleep again in sufficient enough quantities to have the energy to care for her.

When I got home, I realized that the breastfeeding class hadn't helped at all. They had not told me that my husband would have to hold my daughter's flailing arms as I tried unsuccessfully to get her to latch on. They had not mentioned that we'd need to put a tiny bottle of formula in her mouth, get her eating, and rip it out while I shoved my own nipple into her mouth, a technique that seemed crazy, but sometimes worked. They had also said nothing about the importance of the right kind of chair for nursing or the right kind of pillow.

Finally, the class had not mentioned that exhaustion coupled with a baby who had difficulty latching would make me a teary mess every two to three hours when it was time for feeding. I was lucky to get a free, hospital-grade pump, thanks to my insurance, after Colette's latching troubles, but I felt like such a failure every time I used it. I remember going out for a walk with my sister after a particularly difficult time getting Colette to latch, and just sitting down on the curb and bawling. "What am I going to do when I go out in public, when I go to the park, and I see all of these moms nursing and I can't do it? I'll feel like a failure!" I told her. My parents thought I was completely crazy and couldn't understand why I didn't just give her formula. But I was someone who always followed the rules – I ate well, exercised regularly, and tried to lead a healthy lifestyle. I had taken my prenatal vitamins faithfully, even before I got pregnant, had drunk organic milk, and even started eating meat again in order to have enough protein for my developing baby while pregnant, and had not drunk a single glass of wine for nine months. Feed my baby formula? Forget it – "breast is best" is what I'd heard over and over, and my baby would have nothing but the best.

Feeling utterly unprepared and completely desperate, I tried to get help wherever I could. When the hospital sent a visiting nurse to my home to take a look at how my scar was healing, I assaulted her with questions about breastfeeding, asking her to watch as I struggled, and to tell me what I was doing wrong, so I could fix it. At the pediatrician's for our first checkup, I showed the doctor the different techniques I had learned and begged for some advice on what to do. When a friend's mom, who was also a nurse, came to drop off a gift, I sat her down and made her watch me feed as well. Finally, in desperation I called a local branch of the La Leche League, but that involved going to a meeting, and what I needed more than anything was someone who could come into my home. They did point me in the direction of some local lactation consultants who performed home visits, and to my surprise, Carol promised to come right over. She was Lebanese and spoke French, and my French in-laws were there at the time, so there was an instant connection. Assertive and confident, she made me feel that I could surely get Colette to latch with less trouble. She told me that perhaps she had a tight frenulum, but fixing it would require surgery, and she thought that instead I should try some different positions and keep in close touch with her to see how things progressed. Carol also told me I could call her whenever I had a question, and for the first time since I had gotten home, I felt like I was going to be able to handle things.

Slowly but surely, I drove Carol mad with my questions, and consequently drove her away. Luckily, a friend's older sister recommended that I visit a group of lactation consultants at a place called Lactation Care, which was located in a big, beautiful, old home a town away. At that point, my daughter was a few weeks old, and I felt better about travelling with her for help, so I grabbed my husband and headed off for some more advice. An older woman who reminded me of a nun asked us to sit down and explain what was going on. She examined my breasts, undressed my daughter, weighed her, and asked me to feed. When Colette came off the breast, she weighed her again, and told me exactly how many ounces she had consumed. "Your daughter is taking in more milk from this one breast than most babies take from an entire feed," she pronounced. "What you have is an overactive milk supply and a very heavy let-down. Your daughter isn't latching on well because she is getting a huge flood of milk in her mouth every time, and she doesn't like it." She showed me how to massage my breasts to bring the milk forward, gave me a recommendation for a tea to drink that would help me to bring down my milk supply, and once again gave me a number to call with more questions.

Although I did call a number of times, to my surprise, Colette did start to get the hang of breastfeeding and so did I. She learned to latch on, did not require surgery for her frenulum, and became the chubbiest baby I had ever seen. We laughed when some friends told us that their daughter was in the 95th percentile for height and 50th percentile for weight after her checkup – Colette was just the opposite. While her entire body was fat, it was her cheeks that got the most attention. She literally looked like she was going to pop. It was only after her first birthday, when she began to walk, that she started to slim down. It was also at that time that I began to get some perspective on those first few months, and started to see that, as with many things about that first year, time was often the answer to my problems. Colette certainly did have a real problem with latching. But my constant questioning, probing for information, doing everything I could in my power to get answers that worked, only made the situation more frustrating. At school and at work, this strategy had always served me well. But as a parent, I needed to be able to just ride things out, as opposed to figuring them out. I needed to experiment and try to put into practice the advice of others without becoming obsessed with logical answers and solutions.

I think my story answers a lot of the questions you asked, but in terms of the others, see info below:

Having someone who was willing to stick with breastfeeding with me (my husband) was crucial. He was up in the middle of the night at every feed, holding Colette's arms back in the beginning, or whipping out the bottle of formula and shoving her onto my breast those first few weeks when she wouldn't latch. He was there with me every night in the hospital after my c-section, calling for the nurses when I had to feed and couldn't. He was there with me to visit the lactation consultants and to remind me of what they'd said. My parents didn't get why it was so important to me to be able to breastfeed. They would get frustrated with me when I would end up in tears. They didn't want me to suffer and felt like I was torturing myself over something that I didn't need to stress over. There were too many other things to worry about as a new parent, and they didn't get why I was so insistent on making breastfeeding work.

I wish someone had told me that Colette might have trouble latching, and if she did, then I could go to a place like Lactation Care. I wish that I'd had numbers of lactation consultants who would come to my house, so that I didn't have to go searching for that information after Colette was born.

In terms of products that were really helpful, those first few weeks the pump was so important, and also served me well when I went back to work. I was lucky to get a Medela Pump in Style free from my health insurance when Colette had the latch problems, and I know it made pumping a lot easier than it would have been with a less powerful pump. The hands-free bra thing that attached to the pump shields was also wonderful when I was back at work because I could try to sit and do a bit of work while I pumped.

In terms of the internet, I think the kellymom website was very helpful. I also like babycenter. Finally, the Silver Spring Moms yahoo group and Takoma Park Moms yahoo groups have been amazing. Being able to post what I'm going through or a question I have and immediately getting responses back from other moms is wonderful.

What I Wish I Knew About Early Motherhood - Letter to Kathy

I received the following letter from a mom who was about to deliver her second child. She was committed to proper preparation for her baby's birth. She wanted me to understand WHY my working with her would be so important and where she was coming from. As I read her story, I began to understand what breastfeeding means to this mom, and I had thoughts about how, as her lactation consultant, I could help her with her next baby.

She had worked with someone else when she had her first child. She suggested that it was a disaster. Maybe she should have looked around for someone new at the time. That itself can be a hard decision. On balance, now that I know what she was going through, I think I understand better why she didn't.

As I write this, her next child is due in a couple months. We are being careful to get our "ducks in a row" at this point!

May

Our daughter May was born via c-section at 8:00 AM on February 1, at a local hospital. She was full term (39w5d) and came out beautiful and screaming at 8 lbs, 6 oz. Before she was born, she had been breech for a long time, and I had gotten myself used to the idea of a c-section. She finally turned late in the game, but by that point I was huge, uncomfortable, and completely done with being pregnant. The last sonogram we had showed her abdomen measuring about a week ahead, meaning she could be a big baby. My OB mentioned potential complications with delivering big babies, like shoulder dystocia – she really wasn't pushing me one way or the other, but I jumped on the c-section option as a way to avoid all those risks and just have an end date in sight. I never really felt like I was missing out on anything by not going into labor – didn't really feel the need to do much research, yep, pretty naïve. The surgery was easy, she was out quickly, and my physical recovery was great. They let me try to breastfeed her for the first time while I was still in recovery. I was shaking all over from the IV painkillers. The nurse helped me because I was terrified I would drop her. She seemed to know what to do. I remember it seeming like the weirdest feeling in the world.

Before May was born, I didn't really think much about breastfeeding. I was formula fed, as was my husband (and probably most of the other children of the '70s and '80s), and the few friends I have who had babies before me all switched to formula fairly early on. I knew about the benefits of breastmilk and knew I wanted to give it a chance, but I figured if it worked, great, and if not, I'd feed formula. After that first attempt in recovery, I gamely tried to feed her at regular intervals. I didn't feel that overwhelming bonding feeling some mothers say they experience, where it was love at first sight. I felt very protective of her, but at the same time, I felt like I didn't know her very well. And feeding was challenging because of the c-section incision – every time a nurse came in, they would add more pillows and contort my body in strange positions (and I still couldn't feel my legs at this point). I wondered how I would ever do this at home. And then at some point while I was trying to nurse her, she opened her eyes and just stared at me. She had this impish little face, and the look she gave me completely rocked my world. Right then I realized that breastfeeding was going to be way more important to me than I had anticipated.

Unfortunately, it was about that same time that I started to get the feeling that I totally sucked at breastfeeding. On the second day, they weighed her and she had lost a few ounces. They started to warn me about needing to supplement if she lost more weight. I worried about it, but everyone who came by said she was latching fine. So I assumed that the constant sucking, the difficulty keeping her awake, the cracking and the bleeding were all normal. At one point, she spit up blood – it was mine. (She spit up every time she ate. That was a fun thing that continued for six months – but it wasn't reflux, just "happy spitting.") I was in agony, but kept doing what I was doing because I assumed it was just what I had to do to get through. Plus she kept giving me that look.

By the third day, she had lost a few more ounces, and it was really difficult to keep her awake to eat. I was becoming convinced I wasn't making anything for her to eat anyway, and getting increasingly anxious. The lactation consultants at the hospital rearranged more pillows behind me and told me I was doing fine. She spit up more colostrum – they said, "See, she's getting some." The nurses each gave me different advice, and that night the nurse on call said she seemed fine and I should just stick with nursing.

On the fourth day, May's weight was down to 7 lbs 7 oz, and her lips were peeling – the night nurse, who was coming off her shift, said that was a normal newborn thing. That morning a new nurse/lactation consultant came to see me. She immediately told me that May was in serious danger of dehydration, and without supplementation, she could die. I mentioned that the previous night's nurse had said we were doing fine, and she wanted the nurse's name, so she could report her. She relayed stories of babies brought to the PICU with severe dehydration after their parents thought they were "just good sleepers." The term "failure to thrive" got tossed around. She gave me a bunch of Similac samples and told us to take May to the pediatrician on the way home after being discharged. I asked how long I'd have to do this – she said until my milk came in. I'd been asking nurses for the past three days if my milk was in, or how I would know if my milk was in, and nobody could tell me. Now I had one medical professional telling me May was fine, and 20 minutes later, another telling me she was going to die. I was confused, terrified, and felt like my body had failed. I left the baby with my husband and in-laws and went into the shower and cried my eyes out. After we were discharged, we took May to the pediatrician, who told us to supplement after her feedings and gave us some more samples to get us started. We were advised to feed her every three hours (including setting alarms to wake her at night – yeah, that didn't go so well. Poor thing just wanted to sleep.) and bring her back in two days for a weight check.

When we got back to the pediatrician a few days later, she had gained six or seven ounces. The doctor was very excited because it meant, even with all the spit-up, that something was getting where it needed to be – that ruled out more serious issues. I was worried that that "something" was nearly all formula, and I wanted to get her off of it eventually, so when I got home I thumbed through the info packet the hospital had sent me home with, and looked at the list of recommended lactation consultants. First on the list was La Leche League – well, my first thought was "those women are crazy" (Based on what? I have no idea.), so I opted instead to call the more official sounding local hospital's lactation resource. I was thinking that with the local hospital's name in the title, it must be some sort of affiliate, what could be bad? I left a message. The woman who called back listened to my tale and sighed heavily when I got to the part about us having fed formula. I thought she sounded kind of nasty and judgmental, but I was so tired and hormonal that I figured I was being hypersensitive. She said she'd send someone out to my house and that person would call me soon to arrange a time. When she called, she immediately started barking out orders – don't feed her, pump before I get there, get rid of the bottles. She arrived to two barking dogs, a screaming baby, a confused husband, and a completely drained new mom.

The very first thing she did was tell me that any food allergy, illness, or other abnormality that May might experience later in life could be attributed to the three days of formula she had ingested. She told us we should immediately switch pediatricians because ours was a "shill" to the formula company, and that, of course, May had gained weight on formula, too much, because it's full of sugar and promotes obesity. Then she told my husband he was "not supportive" because he didn't go running through the halls of the hospital in the first hours after my delivery to find me a lactation consultant. Then she told me I had to relax because, otherwise, the milk wouldn't let down. Relax, lady? Are you kidding me? I was shaking and crying, and the baby, as was becoming her custom, had sucked for a few minutes and fallen asleep. Somehow my husband showed enough restraint not to cause any bodily harm, and while I lay in bed with May, he quietly paid her and got her out of our house.

The next few weeks were a blur of weight checks and doctor visits, and me reading too many things on the internet. In talking to the handful of people I knew who had breastfed, they all talked to me about happy babies in "milk comas," and feeding off one side at one feeding and the other side the next time, and hooking up to the pump and immediately overflowing four bottles. I was struggling to get an ounce combined, and May had both sides at every feeding, and still needed to supplement. I was losing hope of ever keeping this up, much less ever getting anything in the freezer. I managed to scrape together three ounces for a bottle feeding over the course of probably a week, just in case I ever had to go somewhere without her. Then, at one point, we took May for a test to see if she had pyloric stenosis, which the pediatrician wanted to rule out as a cause of her spitting up. She was weighed on the scale at the specialists' office. I commented to my husband that her weight was the same as it had been a week ago at our doctor's office. He replied that all scales are calibrated slightly differently and that we shouldn't worry. The doctor overheard us and said "she should definitely have gained weight in a week. Are you sure you're making enough milk?" My heart broke into a million pieces. No, I wasn't sure. I wasn't sure of anything except that I was failing my daughter. I started having horrible thoughts like, if this was 150 years ago, she would die. My husband thought I was acting crazy – he didn't see the big deal about formula. Both sets of parents were the same way – just relax and bottle-feed, and everything will be OK. I think the worst part about that time was that, in addition to feeling like a complete failure, I felt completely alone.

When May was about five weeks old, I finally did go visit the La Leche League group close to my home. To my surprise, they were not crazy at all – one of them said to me, "Formula isn't poison, it's food!" They were shocked by how bad my LC experience had been, and they were very welcoming to me. I felt foolish for having judged them so harshly. I wasn't quite ready to whip out my boob in the local restaurant, like the others were doing, but at least I was there. I realized it didn't have to be all or nothing, and I resolved to give May as much nutrition as I could provide through breastmilk and supplement the rest if I had to. But there was this nagging thought in the back of my mind, "WHY can't I make enough on my own? What's wrong with me??" We visited a friend who had just had a baby, and the first thing she asked me was how I cleaned the tubing on my Medela pump because hers was always getting milk in it because she was overflowing the bottles. I burst into tears in her kitchen. I started taking supplements. Before long I had ingested enough fenugreek to bankrupt an Indian restaurant. I smelled like IHOP. And it made May fussy. I drank the tea, ate the cookies, ate oatmeal, drank enough water to move my office into the bathroom, dutifully put the tinctures under my tongue (gagging), and waited the appropriate time to eat or drink. Nothing really made much of a difference in my pumping abilities (personal record – five ounces combined in one session. Whoop-dee-doo!). One of the pediatricians suggested she could prescribe me Reglan – but didn't tell me it had a black box warning. As I was depressed enough without any drugs, I promptly vetoed that one. I was on edge all the time, and my husband and I had some terrible fights – I'm sure he felt I had lost my mind and was pushing him away by being so determined to continue, and so singularly focused on my body being a failure. I felt like he didn't understand what I was going through.

After awhile, we settled into a pattern. May ate, she spit up a lot, I pumped (like crap, but I kept it up). I sent her to daycare with one bottle of formula and the rest breastmilk. She nursed to sleep, and we both really enjoyed our time together. I gave up the supplements. At about six months, she started solids, stopped spitting up, and started sleeping through the night. I was able to start one extra pumping session before I went to bed and finally put some milk in the freezer. I had to fight for every ounce, and every single time I hooked up the pump I was disappointed in the output, but I stuck with it. By the time I went on my first post-baby business trip, I had gotten enough in the freezer that my husband could continue the routine of all breastmilk, except for one formula bottle per day. We kept things going until May was 13 months old and she self-weaned. It's one of the things I'm most proud of in my life, but getting there felt like going through a war. It's had a lasting impact on me. I feel sort of silly even saying that because, overall, I had a pretty easy baby, and I know that people all over the world would give anything to have that.

Today, May is a happy, healthy, beautiful 2½-year-old (she would tell you she's "two years old and a half.") She's in the 90th percentile for weight and off the charts for height. She's a great eater and hardly ever sick (and no allergies either, thank you, crazy lactation consultant!). I doubt she even remembers that we nursed for a year, although I know it stuck with her on some subconscious level because she still likes to crawl into my lap with a cup of milk. Now that it's been more than a year since I weaned and I (finally) have some perspective, I've been able to look back on things. There are some wild cards, like what if I had tried for a vaginal delivery and May had come out when she was good and ready? Would she have been so sleepy? Would her digestive tract have been just that much more developed that she would have kept a bit more of her food down? Would my milk have taken so long to come in? On those points I have no idea – they are some of the reasons I am trying for a VBAC this time, but I also know that realistically I could have had a vaginal birth with the same outcome. I also know that there is a real chance my body just doesn't make enough milk to sustain a baby on its own – I have a fairly small chest, and although I know lots of research says that doesn't matter, maybe it was an issue. But I am convinced that all the back and forth, the stress, the poor advice, and the early supplementing instantly and permanently screwed up whatever supply I was going to have, and I just didn't have the knowledge to ask for the right kind of help to prevent it.

This time around, I want to have the help right from the beginning. I want to know where I stand and what my body is doing, and understand what my options are. I know I have to overcome my own mental hang-ups and realize that there is a chance I will not make enough milk, and try not to feel like a failure about it. I'm scared to go through that part again, and I know I will be holding my breath every time they take our new daughter to be weighed. I want to give myself the best possible chance to have a happy and relaxed experience because I can't put May through seeing me at the low points I was at during her newborn stage, and it's not healthy for me or fair to my husband either. With any luck, I'll get to have the VBAC, my milk will come in faster, there will be enough to go around, and this baby will get her "milk coma." But even if that doesn't happen, I think the right support will go a long way toward making me feel comfortable (and even happy!) with whatever the ultimate outcome is.

Kathy's Thoughts

I don't think I will put any gloss on this letter. I will let it speak for itself.

What I Wish I Knew About Early Motherhood.

You Are Not Alone! An Essay by SS

Despite the fact that women have been breastfeeding since the beginning of time, there are insufficient resources available to the modern day woman who seeks to breastfeed her child. When I had my first child six years ago, I did not know breastfeeding would hurt. I know, silly me. But where in the books I read did it say that it would hurt? And hurt a lot? The books talked about getting the proper latch and remedies for cracked or sore nipples, but no one said it would feel like someone is taking your nipple and hammering down on it with a pick ax. I also didn't know that it was possible my daughter could be tongue-tied and that this could affect my ability to breastfeed her.

With my first daughter, I was in so much pain. Not only were my nipples sore, but there was an electrifying pain that would spread through my breasts as she would suck. During a group breastfeeding session at the hospital, one of the consultants noticed that my daughter's tongue was tied, and her tongue was not coming out of her mouth. In a way I was relieved because I thought, "Well this is why I'm having so much more trouble" than other women. I was a successful professional – how could I not be able to do something as basic as breastfeeding. When I got home from the hospital, I was so sore (and bloody) that I told my husband to get out the formula. He returned to me with the breast pump we had purchased and said, "Try this first." So I did.

The breast pump didn't hurt as much as breastfeeding, so I pumped every two hours and gave him the bottles to feed her. I would wake up in the night and pump, and give him the bottles. I rarely fed the baby myself. Looking back, this was awfully isolating. Not only could I not bond with the baby while breastfeeding her, I wasn't bonding with her at all.

Our pediatrician advised us we could have her frenulum clipped, but that he did not do this procedure, so he recommended a doctor who would. The doctor was very nice and encouraging, extolling the virtues of breastfeeding. He told me to call him to let him know how things turned out. Unfortunately, the clipping did not help. I was too embarrassed to call the doctor to tell him. I had failed again. I decided to pump exclusively.

Although the breast pump didn't hurt as much as breastfeeding, it still hurt. My areola was red and sore, but it didn't hurt as much as the breastfeeding, and so I pressed on. It wasn't until I went to a breastfeeding center in DC that I found out I could buy larger breast shields. I had been using the 24 mm breast shields that came with the pump. The stores likes Babies R Us and Buy Buy Baby did not sell the larger breast shields at the time (2005). The 27 mm flanges improved my comfort level a little bit.

The upside to pumping was that it gave me freedom. Although I had to be home every two to three hours to pump, I could go out without the baby without worrying that she'd be hungry. At night I would go longer stretches and slept five to seven hours a night, while my husband gave the baby bottles whenever she was hungry.

I used to stress about wasted milk. With my first daughter, I was lucky enough to pump five to six ounces per breast per pumping session. If I expended the energy and suffered the pain to pump it, I wanted her to eat it. Every time I saw an ounce go down the drain I would cringe. I was very unhappy during those first few months. Looking back, I probably had postpartum depression and just didn't know it. I wasn't contemplating killing myself or my child, but I thought my daughter didn't like me and that she only liked her dad. He was the one feeding her after all.

When I went back to work, three months after my daughter was born, I finally gave up. I wasn't accustomed to taking my clothes off at work, and there was no lock on the door. I was self-conscious the whole time and lasted only one or two days. I was a little disappointed in myself, but at the same time, I had to give myself credit for pumping exclusively for those three months, even though it hurt.

With my second daughter, I was determined to breastfeed. My husband was somewhat skeptical. Wouldn't I have the same problems as with our first daughter? I couldn't imagine that I'd have two children who were tongue-tied. That would be like lightening striking twice.

When my second daughter was born, I was mentally prepared for the pain. I knew what I would have to endure. I checked her tongue, and it didn't look the same as my first daughter's, so I thought I was in the clear. Thankfully, this time I did not have the electrifying pain shooting through my breasts. It was only nipple pain/soreness. I told myself I could get through this. Everyone said, "Give it two weeks." Well for me, it took three weeks before the serious soreness went away. Thank goodness for the percocet because that took the edge off and let me get through those first few weeks.

I used lanolin after every feeding. I constantly checked to make sure she was latched properly. I took her off my breast and started again if I suspected she was not properly latched. I said, "Big mouth. Give mommy big mouth" more times than I'd like to admit. I wouldn't put her on my breast unless I felt her mouth was open wide enough. I got frustrated when she wouldn't open wide.

Although I asked the hospital's lactation consultant about renting a pump, she cautioned me that I shouldn't give the baby a bottle until at least three to four weeks because the baby may not want to breastfeed if she knows she can get milk easier from a bottle. I was a little disappointed by this because I knew myself and knew I would want the freedom the pump would allow me. Would it really hinder my ability to breastfeed? I was willing to take the risk, so my husband went to the store and bought me a breast pump.

As soon as I got home from the hospital, I started pumping. Pumping gave my nipples a rest and a chance to heal. I could alternate breastfeeding with pumping or I could pump as much as I wanted, as needed. I started to get a little too used to pumping, so I had to make a conscious effort to start every day breastfeeding my daughter. Otherwise, I could go an entire day without breastfeeding the baby even once. Pumping also gave me extra milk. Every time I breastfed, I subsequently pumped whatever was left.

I didn't produce as much milk per breast as I had with my first child. This time I got two ounces per breast every two hours. Thankfully, this child does not eat as much as my first child, so four ounces a feeding is enough. However, although I didn't have to worry about making enough milk, I did have to worry about how my daughter was reacting to my milk. For the first couple of weeks, the baby spit up at every feeding – sometimes through her nose. She seemed to keep most of it down, but she would cry in pain, sometimes for hours – and this was not normal. My husband suggested I keep a food diary. Even though I knew this was for the baby's well-being, I resented this. I decided to take dairy out of my diet to see if it made a difference – and it did. There was a complete turn around. The baby still spits up occasionally – what baby doesn't? But it's minimal, and she rarely cries due to gas pain these days. Of course, that's because I also gave up tomato sauce and onions in addition to the dairy. I've numbered the bottles, and I now write down what foods I ate before pumping, so we can monitor whether there are any other foods that don't sit well with her.

When my daughter was four weeks, my husband had a vasectomy. After dropping my older daughter off at school, I drove my husband to the surgery center, which was 40 minutes from our house. I was a little nervous because I knew we were going to be at the surgery center for a while and I had never breastfed in public. I didn't know if I'd have the courage to do it. To add to my stress, I knew I was going to need to pump after breastfeeding or my breasts would get painfully swollen. So in addition to a couple of bottles full of milk, I brought my breast pump with me. I figured I'd hold out as long as I could, and then go to my car to pump. I'd be more comfortable pumping in a car rather than breastfeeding? There's something wrong with that!

While I was sitting there in the surgery center waiting room, I realized I wasn't comfortable breastfeeding there, so I gave the baby a bottle and started to think about where I should go to pump. I remembered that there was a breastfeeding center a couple of blocks away, so I took the chance and called to ask if they'd let me pump there. They said yes, but they had a full class going on at that time, so they set me up in the front of the store area with a tall screen and I pumped away while mothers and fathers came to purchase products and supplies. The cash register was only a couple of feet away from me, but somehow, once I walked into the breastfeeding center I was safe. I got so energized while I was there that I gave a pep talk to a new mother who was suffering from sore nipples. I told her everything that I had done for my nipples, reminded her that she is not alone, and told her to hang on for a few more weeks. That it really is true – it does get easier/less painful – but that she has to take care of her nipples and herself.

After pumping, I returned to the surgery center only to find out that my husband's recovery was taking longer than expected and that we would need to be there a few more hours. I still wasn't comfortable breastfeeding there, so I gave the baby another bottle. By the time I needed to pump again, I had made friends with the front desk nurses. With my newfound confidence, I told them I needed to pump, and they set me up in an empty office. Voila!

Later that day I kept thinking about how energized I felt by my experience at the breastfeeding center – it was the sense of sisterhood. I reviewed the schedule to see when I could visit there again for a breastfeeding class, but decided to investigate whether there was a class closer to where I live. After shooting off a few emails to the nearby lactation consultants, I found that there wasn't anything closer.

Since I was finding it hard to get myself and the baby together to go back to the breastfeeding center, after five weeks I went to see a lactation consultant because I wanted some encouragement and confidence in the way I was breastfeeding. I was concerned others would look at me and say, "Hey, you're not doing that correctly." I don't know what took me so long to see a lactation consultant. I should have done it sooner – before I even had the baby. I write this to save you from the trouble. If you don't have one, go find a consultant who understands your needs and can help you be successful in your quest to breastfeed your child. You don't have to do this alone.

The lactation consultant introduced me to a hospital-grade pump. Prior to buying my pump, I read some reviews online where the women wrote they didn't see much of a difference. So why pay more money to rent when I can buy one? I didn't find any documented facts that stated what a hospital-grade pump can do that other pumps cannot. Now that I've tried the hospital-grade pump, I see that it is much easier on the nipples and more efficient. Another recommendation the lactation consultant made was to switch from the 27 mm breast shield to a 30 mm breast shield. The 30 mm breast shield was more comfortable, and I haven't used the 27 mm breast shield since.

But the best product the lactation consultant gave me was a well-made hands-free pumping bra. Before that bra, I was doing one breast at a time, and I could barely turn the page of my book without spilling milk (and yes, you can cry over spilled milk). Now I can read, write, drink, or eat while I pump, so I don't feel so tethered.

When I told my lactation consultant that my store-bought pump didn't have a strong enough suction to suck both nipples at the same time, she told me to call the manufacturer to ask for a new pump. I called the manufacturer, and they wanted me to demonstrate how I was pumping over the phone, so they could troubleshoot. While I appreciate that they're willing to do that, I was not willing. So after a bit of wrangling, the representative agreed to send me new parts to try, including the tubes, to see if that fixes the problem. I haven't had the courage to put my nipples back into the store-bought pump, knowing the hospital-grade pump is so much easier on them.

I also mentioned to the representative that it would be nice if they sold their pumps with different size breast shields – small, medium, large, extra-large. She told me that the 24 mm is the standard size and that's why they only sell them with 24 mm. I told her that most women don't know they need a different size, so they use what comes with the pump. It costs extra to buy larger shields and some women don't have the luxury to buy the various sizes to see which size fits best. She told me that the lactation consultants measure women in the hospital. I told her I'd had two babies in hospitals and saw lactation consultants at both, and neither measured me or told me I may need larger breast shields. She told me that if a purchaser needs a larger breast shield size, the company sends a complimentary pair. I told her I didn't know that since the company did not mention that in the pamphlets they provide with the pump. How would anyone know this??? At least with this child, they sell the larger shields in the store, so women can see that larger sizes exist. In 2005, it was a secret that larger shields even existed!

I question why I still struggle with breastfeeding in public. My mind wanders to the baby's second week when my parents were visiting. My sister and mom told me I had to go upstairs to breastfeed because my dad was in the living room. And it was my house! At the time I listened to them and I'm still annoyed that they didn't support me to breastfeed in "public." Why do we have to hide to feed our babies? Why is it okay for me to breastfeed in front of a complete stranger, but not my own family?

At seven weeks, my nipples are no longer sore, but breastfeeding still hurts a little, particularly during the first minute. After the first minute, the pain subsides, and it's just a little uncomfortable. At times, I don't notice it at all. And it turns out this daughter also is tongue-tied – just not to the extent my first daughter was. I'm glad I didn't know she was tongue-tied because I may not have gotten this far.

I try not to stress when she doesn't drink the full bottle. I get frustrated, but I've learned to let it go. For a week or so, I was leaving the freshly pumped milk out on the counter with an ice pack, so that if she didn't finish the bottle, I could stick the leftover milk in the fridge for a future feeding. But she really likes her milk warmed, and if the milk is warmed I don't think you're supposed to reuse it, so it goes down the drain. Such is life.

Every day is a new day. I do the best I can. We all do. If you can't breastfeed, you're not a bad mom. You need to do what's best for you. If you're miserable, the baby will be, too. But before you give up, reach out and find some support. You are not alone.

Conclusion by DS

There's no way to thoroughly prepare for how life-altering having a new baby is. As I write this conclusion, my son is almost two years old, and I can't believe how quickly those years have gone. I vividly remember moments in the first few months when I was utterly convinced I was losing my mind, only to realize that I was simply exhausted. I knew a good chunk of sleep would fix almost everything, but who can get that with a newborn in the house? In my saner moments, I sincerely considered putting a Post-It note bearing "This too shall pass" on every wall of my house, to reassure myself that things would change. So, looking back with a little bit of perspective, here's what I hope you can hear from my experiences and those of the other moms in this book: You will make it. Things will get better. The first few months will be harder than anything you've ever done. They will also be more rewarding than anything you've ever done, and that will only multiply as you add on more months and years of watching your child grow and delight in discovering the world.

Nothing lasts forever (not even the good stuff, like when the kid finally gets on a schedule that really works for all of you). Sleep is crucial. So is a good support network. So is knowing that you have what it takes to be a good mother to your child. Read the books, listen to the advice, but use what works for you and leave the rest behind – and respectfully give other moms the right to do the same for their families! There are so many ways to raise children, and most of them will do fine by your kids as long as you love them unconditionally and have their best interests at heart. Cherish the good moments, endure the bad ones, and keep the end in mind – you are raising a little human being who, one day when you lay him down for his nap and tell him, "Sleep well, little one; I love you," will take his pacifier out and answer "Love you!" as you walk out the door. The world is a never-ending source of fascinating new adventures for my toddler, and I promise you, getting to be part of it has been worth every sleepless night, every moment of doubt or fear, every bit of physical and emotional pain that comes with bearing and rearing a child. I wouldn't trade it for anything (although, in the spirit of honesty and full disclosure of this book, I must confess that I might start loaning him out cheaply if he throws a new box of pasta in the dog's water bowl one more time!). Enjoy some skin-to-skin naps, take lots of pictures and write notes for the baby book, ask for and accept help, and above all, don't forget to fall in love with your newest family member.

Resources

Books

Huggins, K. (2010). *The Nursing Mother's Companion.* Boston, MA: Harvard Common Press.

McCue, K. (2010). *Start Here: Breastfeeding and Infant Care with Humor and Common Sense* (my first book). Amarillo, TX: Hale Publishing.

Mohrbacher, N., & Kendall-Tackett, K. (2010). *Breastfeeding Made Simple: Seven Natural Laws for Nursing Mothers.* Oakland, CA: New Harbinger Publications.

Renfrew, M., Fisher, C., & Arms, S. (2000). *Bestfeeding: Getting Breastfeeding Right for You.* New York: Celestial Arts.

Sears, M., & Sears, W. (2000). *The Breastfeeding Book: Everything You Need to Know About Nursing Your Child from Birth Through Weaning.* New York, NY: Little, Brown and Company.

Wiessinger, D., West, D., & Pitman, T. (2010). *The Womanly Art of Breastfeeding.* New York: Ballantine Books.

Websites

http://www.breastfeed.com/

http://www.breastfeeding.com/

http://www.breastfeedingonline.com/

http://www.cdc.gov/breastfeeding/resources/guide.htm

http://www.gotmom.org/

http://www.kellymom.com/

http://www.lalecheleague.org/

http://www.womenshealth.gov/breastfeeding/

Organizations

PACE (Parent and Community Education)

Your local hospital may have a mothers' support group. Ask someone in the lactation department when you're an in-patient.

Twitter & Facebook

There are some excellent research-based Twitter Posts and Facebook Pages which can be fun to investigate.

My own twitter account is AllBabyBasics.

Author Bio

Kathleen F. McCue, RN, MS, FNP, IBCLC, is both a nurse practitioner and a board-certified lactation consultant. She is the mother of two grown children and currently lives in Bethesda, Maryland. She has been working in the medical field since 1976 when she first graduated nursing school. Presently, she works part time as a nurse practitioner for a pediatric practice, Children First  Pediatrics, and part time operating a full-service lactation consulting business - Bethesda Breastfeeding, LLC - in the Washington, DC, area.

Kathleen's first exposure to breastfeeding and its benefits came nearly 20 years ago when she was working as a nurse in a local pediatric practice. She saw that breastfeeding offered a wide range of health advantages, but it had little public recognition and acceptance. Working with breastfeeding mothers and babies offered Kathleen a great deal of personal satisfaction. In 2000, Kathleen returned to school for her Nurse Practitioner (NP) degree, and chose Family Practice as her specialty. NP training brought new information and insight that Kathleen immediately put to good use with new mothers. At the same time, her expanded experience and confidence helped bring greater reassurance and calm to women seeking to breastfeed for the first time.

Although breastfeeding outcomes and infant health issues are serious, Kathleen has found that new mothers benefit from understanding they are not alone and from hearing about innumerable other women who have faced the same issues. She uses the humor of shared human experience to help new moms cope. There will always be another situation or predicament that is more unusual, more unique, or otherwise just able to make a mom under stress lighten up and laugh. With humor, Kathleen helps put new moms at ease, while constantly reassuring them that breastfeeding can and will work, and that relaxing can actually facilitate the process.

Kathleen wanted to write a book where mothers shared their intimate thoughts and valuable ideas among each other. There were clinical days when Kathleen wished she could have called the mother she had worked with in the morning and asked if she would discuss her feelings and fears with the mother she was working with in the afternoon. Of course, because of HIPAA laws and general common sense, Kathleen knew this would be infeasible; hence the book concept was born.

Kathleen loves to hear from new parents! Feel free to stay in touch with her on Twitter: @AllBabyBasics and on Facebook: AllBabyBasics. Her website can be found at www.bethesdabreastfeeding.com.

Ordering Information

Hale Publishing, L.P.

1712 N. Forest Street

Amarillo, Texas, USA 79106

8:00 am to 5:00 pm CST

Call » 806.376.9900

Toll free » 800.378.1317

Fax » 806.376.9901

Online Orders

www.ibreastfeeding.com